DATE DUE

THE EARTH'S CRUST AND MANTLE

Developments in Solid Earth Geophysics

Developments in Solid Earth Geophysics

1

THE EARTH'S CRUST AND MANTLE

by

F.A. VENING MEINESZ

Emeritus professor of Geophysics,
Geodesy and Cartography at the State University, Utrecht
and the Technical University, Delft
(The Netherlands)

ELSEVIER PUBLISHING COMPANY

AMSTERDAM - LONDON - NEW YORK

1964

ELSEVIER PUBLISHING COMPANY
335 JAN VAN GALENSTRAAT, P.O. BOX 211, AMSTERDAM

AMERICAN ELSEVIER PUBLISHING COMPANY, INC.
52 VANDERBILT AVENUE, NEW YORK, N.Y. 10017

ELSEVIER PUBLISHING COMPANY LIMITED
12B, RIPPLESIDE COMMERCIAL ESTATE
RIPPLE ROAD, BARKING, ESSEX

LIBRARY OF CONGRESS CATALOG CARD NUMBER 64-12611
WITH 24 ILLUSTRATIONS

PREFACE

This short history of the earth's crust and mantle is not meant to be a complete geophysical treatise on these parts of the earth. It is not, for example, a special study of the relative movements of the continents, although that subject is dealt with. Moreover, it does not discuss geomagnetism, which is probably caused by currents in the core.

An important part of this book is devoted to deformations of the crust, which are attributed to mantle currents. It is clear that these currents may affect the figure of the earth and disturb its equilibrium. On the one hand, therefore, the subjects discussed touch on geology, and on the other on geodesy. In order to make the book more accessible to geologists the writer has, with the exception only of the case of the external gravity field up to great distances from the earth, avoided mathematical treatment; otherwise, for the basic theory and related considerations, the reader should refer to HEISKANEN and VENING MEINESZ (1958) or to other papers.

If this short book proves to be of use to geophysicists, geologists, physical geographers and physical geodesists, the writer will feel richly rewarded.

Amersfoort, The Netherlands   F. A. VENING MEINESZ
May, 1964

v

CONTENTS

PREFACE V

CHAPTER I. INTRODUCTION AND SUMMARY 1

CHAPTER II. CONSTITUTION OF THE EARTH, ISOSTASY, EQUILIBRIUM, THERMAL

BEHAVIOUR 7

1. Constitution of the earth and thermal behaviour 7
2. Isostasy 10
3. The equilibrium figure of the earth and the geodetic problem of deriving
   the figure of the earth from gravity 25
4. The external gravity field of the earth 27
5. Active volcanicity a cause of deviations from equilibrium 34

CHAPTER III. CRUSTAL PHENOMENA AND DEFORMATIONS 35

1. General effect of horizontal compression in the crust 35
2. Plastic down-buckling of the crust; the origin of geosynclines 35
3. Further history of the geosynclinal areas and their forelands 37
4. Effects of horizontal tension in the crust 42
5. Belts of crustal wrench faulting usually accompanied by overriding . . 44
6. The crustal deformation in island-arc areas 47
7. Crustal phenomena and deformations in the ocean crust 51

CHAPTER IV, CONVECTION CURRENTS IN THE MANTLE 57

1. Arguments in favour of mantle convection currents 57
2. The transition layer between 500 and 900 km depth in connection with
   mantle currents 59
3. Spherical harmonic development of the earth's topography 61
4. Interpretation of the spherical harmonic developments, history of the
   earth 65
5. The present phase, third phase, of the earth's history, a crystalline mantle 68
6. A possible explanation of the 5th order spherical harmonic prevailing
   during the present phase of the earth's history, the third phase 69
7. The episodic half-turn currents in the mantle 71
8. Smaller types of mantle currents. 73
9 Deep basins in island-arc areas; third arcs. 73
10. Movements of continents relative to the poles and to each other . . . 75
    Appendix 77

CHAPTER V. THE PATTERN OF MANTLE CURRENTS, OF DEEP OCEAN TRENCHES

AND OF VOLCANOES OVER THE EARTH'S SURFACE 79

1. Rising mantle currents below the continents and mid-ocean ridges . . . 79
2. The pattern of the convection currents in the mantle 81
3. The two types of deep ocean trenches and their distribution over the earth 97
4. The distribution of volcanoes over the earth's surface 104
5. Mountain formation on the continents 113
REFERENCES 115
INDEX 119

LIST OF FIGURES

Fig.   Page

II.1   Local isostatic gravity anomalies and volcanoes in the Indonesian archipelago . . . . 13—18

II.2   Regional isostatic gravity anomalies, geology and earthquakes . . 19—24

III.1 Plastic crustal downbuckling of oceanic crust on true vertical scale . . 36

III.2 Five successive stages of Kuenen's experiments on buckling of a floating plastic layer under uniaxial horizontal compression 37

III.3 Profiles through the Alps. 38

III.4 The melting and flowing away of the down-buckled root of the Alps 40

III.5 The development of a graben 42

III.6 Location of the crests of submarine median ridges and rises compared with the geometrical median line of the ocean basins. 53

III.7 Free-air anomalies and the deduced crustal structure under the Mendocino fracture zone 54

IV.1   Spherical harmonic development of the earth's topography 64

IV.2   Ordinates of Fig.IV.1, multiplied by $n^{\frac{1}{2}}(n+1)^{\frac{1}{2}}$ 66

IV.3   First-order current in a fluid undifferentiated earth during an early stage of its history 67

IV.4   Schematic representation of the currents in a crystalline mantle . . . 70

V.1   Epicenters of normal earthquakes from 1930 to 1941 82

V.2   Structural map of South America 84

V.3   Structural map of Central America and the Antilles 85

V.4   Structural map of North America 87

V.5   Structural map of Eurasia 91

V.6   Structural map of Africa 93

V.7   Gravity profile: Java—Indian Ocean over Soerakarta 96

V.8   Gravity profile: Indian Ocean—Sumatra over Benkoelen 98

V.9   Gravity profile: Strait Surigao—Pacific Ocean over the Mindanao Trench 99

V.10   Map Korea—New Guinea, showing the distribution of volcanoes . . 102

V.11   Map showing the distribution of volcanoes over the earth . . .105—108

Chapter I

INTRODUCTION AND SUMMARY

In this short review of our knowledge of the crust and the mantle of the earth, looked at from the geophysical side, the writer will mention only briefly the basic facts and considerations on which our knowledge is founded; but the literature where data and details can be found will be indicated, at least so far as geophysical measurements and lines of thought are concerned. Many data will also be provided by geology and physical geography; the reader will have no difficulty in finding literature on these aspects.

The geophysical data bearing on the subject will be given mainly by accurate gravity measurements and seismological registrations. Since we shall not consider the earth's core, geomagnetic data do not contribute appreciably to the subject. As is well known, the seismological data provide valuable information about the surfaces of discontinuity in the earth, and about the densities. The gravity observations give indications about the way in which the masses in the earth are distributed, and likewise about deviations from equilibrium in the earth. In this way they provide important information about the forces working in the earth.

In Chapter II, Section 1, we shall deal with the current views about the constitution of the different parts of the earth, and mention the densities concerned. We shall also consider the thermal behaviour of the earth. In Section II.2 of the same Chapter, we shall deal with the principle of isostasy and the readjustment of isostatic equilibrium. In Section II.3, we shall discuss the problem of the equilibrium figure which the earth would assume if no disturbances were present, and the geodetic problem of deriving the geoid, which is the actual figure of the earth, from gravity data. If the formula for normal gravity is chosen in harmony with the equilibrium figure, the gravity anomalies may be considered as indicating deviations of the earth from equilibrium, and the same is true for the deviations of the geoid from the earth's equilibrium figure. These deviations obviously have great importance for the geophysicist. In Section II.4, the external gravity field and the corresponding equipotential surfaces will be dealt with.

In Section II.5, the effects of active volcanicity, in which is found one source of disturbances of equilibrium of the earth, will be examined.

In Chapter III, we shall discuss crustal phenomena. In Section III.1, we shall examine the general effects of horizontal compression of the rigid crust and the field of positive gravity anomalies thus created. In Section III.2, we shall deal with

1

another effect of horizontal compression in the crust, i.e., the giving way of the crust by plastic down-buckling in geosynclinal belts, thus causing belts of strong negative anomalies. In Section III.3, we shall pursue the history of these belts after the disappearance of the horizontal compression. In the continents, high mountain ranges came into being; in the oceans, the trenches that formed during the first stage disappeared, and low ridges took their places. Subcrustal currents carried off the mountain roots; this led to the eventual disappearance of the continental mountain ridges and to the gradual formation of a broad belt of Mittelgebirge in the foreland of the mountain ranges. At the same time, strong erosional processes attacked the mountain ranges.

In Section III.4, we shall examine the effect of horizontal tension in the crust, or at least of stress release. We shall find that this leads to the formation of graben and horsts. We shall give the results of the computation of the magnitude of the elevations and depressions thus created. As a striking example of these phenomena we shall discuss the belt of lakes and volcanoes in Africa, which runs from Lake Nyasa to the Red Sea and the Dead Sea.

In Section III.5, we shall consider horizontal shear movements along huge fault planes through the crust (wrench faulting), which in many cases are accompanied by the overriding of the crustal block on one side of the plane by the block on the other side. This leads to an asymmetrical gravity disturbance, giving a belt with positive anomalies on the high side and with negative anomalies on the low side. We shall also consider the evidence of such wrench-faulting belts without the occurrence of overriding of one crustal block by the other. This last phenomenon is not accompanied by earthquakes, whilst the first is usually particularly active seismically.

Both types of crustal deformation, as will be dealt with in Section III.2 and Section III.5, occur in island arcs (see Section III.6). We shall find that an extensive field of uniaxial compression in the crust can bring about plastic yielding of the crust by downbuckling, as will be discussed in Section III.2, in belts making angles of about 55° with the direction of compression – which is in accordance with the theory of Bijlaard – and that it can also cause wrench faulting with overriding in belts making angles of 25—30° with this direction, as will be dealt with in Section III.5; it then obeys the laws of shear as given by ANDERSON (1951), KING HUBBERT, (1951), and others. In island arcs, we shall find the down-buckled belts in the central parts of the arc—in the Indonesian arc it is the belt south of Java, continuing to the Tanimbar Islands—and the wrench faulting with overriding in the wing parts of the arc; in the Indonesian arc, these are the belts to the west of Sumatra and to the east of the Philippine Islands.

In Section III.7, the crustal deformations in the ocean crust will be dealt with.

Extensive fields of uniaxial compression in the crust, bringing about island arcs, or tension in the crust causing graben and horsts, cannot be explained by all-sided compression in the crust, such as would arise from shrinking of the earth through cooling. It is difficult to account for them in any other way than by mantle currents, and, in view of the great dimensions of the island arcs, we have to assume that these currents take place over the full thickness of the mantle of 2865 km.

In Chapter IV, we shall deal with such currents as are likely to have the character of convection currents induced by the cooling of the earth by radiation from its surface. We shall find that, besides the arguments in favour of this hypothesis derived from the crustal phenomena which will be mentioned in Chapter III, there are many other reasons for accepting this hypothesis. They will be considered in Section IV.1. The writer thinks that the number of arguments is such and their force so convincing that we can be almost certain that the hypothesis of mantle convection currents is true.

In Section IV.2, we shall cope with the difficulty that between the depths of 500 and 900 km the density of the mantle increases by about 0.7 g/cm^3 more than can be accounted for by the increase in pressure. This, therefore, indicates a gradual change in the matter in this layer. How is a convection current able to break through this layer? The solution can probably be found by assuming that in this layer the olivine, which is the main constituent of the upper mantle, changes from the orthorhombic phase to the cubic phase, and that, therefore, the lower 2000 km of the mantle consists mainly of spinel. In Section IV.2, we shall mention an important study on this matter by MEIJERING and ROOYMANS (1958). In this Section we shall likewise point out the highly increased instability of the mantle caused by the presence of this transition layer.

In Section IV.3, we shall deal with the spherical harmonic development of the earth's topography. For each order n, a representative figure of the $2n + 1$ sub-terms of this order is found by deriving the root mean square of the topographic elevations, as given by all the sub-terms of this order. In this way, a curve can be derived which gives this representative ordinate for each value of n. The same development will also be carried out for the submarine topography alone; for this development the continental topography will be put at zero. From the two developments mentioned it is easy to obtain a third one for the continental topography alone, putting the submarine topography at zero.

In Section IV.4, and, for the higher orders, in Section IV.8, we shall try to interpret the results of these three spherical harmonic developments; thus we will find remarkable indications about three phases of the earth's history. We will be led to surmise that in the earliest phase of this history the core did not exist, and that a central convection current brought the heavy metals towards the centre, thus gradually forming the core; an ur-continent was formed at the surface. After the core had formed, mantle convection currents came into being and caused the urt continent to break up into parts which are more or less identical to the presencontinents. In the topography represented by these continents, the third and fourth order spherical harmonics prevailed. We must assume that in this period the mantle matter probably had more or less the properties of a Newtonian fluid, although probably with a high viscosity.

It is likely that since that early period the mantle crystallized; this led to the third phase of the earth's history, which will be dealt with in Section IV.5. One important argument in favour of the hypothesis that the mantle is now crystalline is provided by the supposition, mentioned above, that the transition layer between the depths of 500 and 900 km can be explained as a layer in which the orthorhombic phase of the olivine changes to the cubic phase of spinel. A second argument is provided by the episodicity[1] of the mantle convection currents, which followed from the episodic occurrence, at least during the more recent geological history of the earth, of periods of orogenesis which bring about folding and overthrusting of the rocks in geosynclines. Between these periods, the earth's crust appears to be quiet for a fairly long time of a few hundred million years; no mantle currents seem to exert drag forces on the crust. We can understand this behaviour for a mantle that is crystalline. In that case, the unstable character of the mantle, caused by the earth's radiation and cooling at the surface, cannot lead to convection currents in the mantle, unless horizontal temperature gradients cause pressure gradients large enough to overcome the atomic forces in the crystals and to bring about pseudo-flow movements in the mantle. This leads to a half-turn convection current, bringing down the outer mantle layer of low temperature and relatively high density and bringing up the lower mantle layer of high temperature and relatively small density. The dynamic equilibrium is then re-established and a quiet period starts. This lasts until the upper mantle layer has cooled down again by heat loss and the lower layer has been warmed up by the high-temperature core. A new period of half-turn convection currents can then start. As will be discussed in the last part of Section IV.8, this is preceded and prepared by mantle currents of smaller type. The whole process of alternating orogenic and quiet periods in the crust and mantle is clearly episodic, but not necessarily periodic. This is in good harmony with the findings of geologists. The half-turn convection currents will be dealt with in Section IV.7.

A further reason for assuming that the mantle is now crystalline is provided by the fact that the spherical harmonic curve for the total topography shows a fairly large 5th order term, which is also found in the curve for the continents, but is much less pronounced in the curve for the submarine topography. There is reason to suppose that this term represents the topography of the geosynclinal belts over the earth's surface; we know that this topography is large in the continental and

---

[1] By the term *episodicity* the writer wishes to indicate that the mantle currents, causing orogeny at the earth's surface, occur during certain time intervals separated by unequal time intervals of rest. The episodes of mantle currents and orogeny are, therefore, not exactly periodic; this is denoted as an episodic occurrence.

small in the oceanic geosynclines. In Section IV.6, we shall deal with the possible explanation of this 5th order character of the mantle convection current distribution for a crystalline mantle. This will also explain why in the present period of the earth's history the horizontal compression in the crust leads to compression in geosynclinal belts and not in broader shields, as e.g., must have been the case in the early part of the earth's history when the ur-continent was pushed together.

In Section IV.8, the occurrence in the mantle of smaller convection cells will be dealt with, and this will lead to the treatment in Section IV.9, of the origin of the deep basins in island-arc areas and of third arcs in those areas.

In Chapter V, we shall try to apply our knowledge to the earth as it is now. We shall attempt to use the facts about the earth's topography, which nowadays are also fairly good for the oceanic parts of the earth's surface, in order to derive a pattern for the convection currents which are supposed to be going on in the mantle. The seismicity of the earth's upper layers clearly points to activity of the earth in the present period. In Section V.1, we shall make mention of the topography found by the oceanographers of the Lamont Geological Observatory and of the Scripps Institution of Oceanography over the mid-ocean rises. A map of these rises, published by MENARD (1958), shows their distribution over the earth's surface. Graben were found on the top of several of these mid-ocean rises, and this points to these rises occurring above rising mantle currents, which cause the crustal tension needed for graben formation. Two other arguments give similar indications. In the first place, these rises are usually characterized by higher vertical temperature gradients in the surface layers of the crust than elsewhere, and this likewise points to a rising mantle current below them. The third argument is connected with the fact that we must also expect rising currents below the continents. This is based on the higher radioactivity of the sial constituting the continents compared with the basalt and the olivine forming the oceanic crust. So, we may assume that there are higher temperatures below the continents than below the adjoining parts of the oceans, and this must lead to the prevalence of rising convection currents below the borders of the continents and of subsiding currents below the adjoining oceanic areas. The oceans are, however, too wide to overlie only subsiding convection currents, and so we must expect that farther away from the continents, areas of rising currents must also occur. We will thus arrive at the third argument in favour of the view that the mid-ocean rises are found above rising mantle currents.

On the basis of Menard's map of the mid-ocean rises and of the distribution of the continents, as well as of the distribution of the geosynclinal belts of recent origin, we shall, in Section V.2, make an attempt to find the pattern of convection currents in the mantle. This will give us a starting point for a study of the crustal deformations caused by the drag exerted by these currents on the crust. In Section V.3, we shall study the oceanic parts of the crust and make a sub-division of the deep trenches into central trenches and wing trenches, so-called because of their mode of occurrence in island arcs.

In Section V.4, we shall deal with the distribution of volcanoes over the earth's surface. In general, we can say that they occur where the cohesion of the rigid crust is sufficiently disturbed to allow the magma to pass and reach the earth's surface. Since fault planes through the crust are obviously never absolutely plane, relative movements of the crustal blocks on the two sides of such a surface may cause volcanic activity, but plastic deformation of the crust does not necessarily lead to this.

In Section V.5, there will be a short summary of the subject of mountain formation in the continents. Based on the views developed in the previous Chapters, the writer will tentatively attempt to give a classification according to the different processes leading to the topography in the continents. The writer does not feel himself in a position to apply this to all the present topography. A few examples will be mentioned.

Chapter II

CONSTITUTION OF THE EARTH, ISOSTASY, EQUILIBRIUM, THERMAL BEHAVIOUR

1. *Constitution of the earth and thermal behaviour*

Speaking in broad terms, the earth consists of three parts. Down to a depth of about 35 km we have the rigid crust, below that and to a depth of about 2900 km is the mantle, and below that the core. We shall consider these parts in more detail and deal with their constitution and thermal behaviour.

The core is assumed mainly to consist of metals, especially iron and nickel. It has a high temperature of at least a few thousands of degrees. It is supposed to be subject to currents of a velocity of the order of a few hundreds of kilometres per year. These currents of matter are assumed also to have an electrical character and thus to be responsible for the geomagnetic field of the earth. They are subject to the Coriolis effect brought about by the earth's rotation, and this causes the geomagnetic poles to have a tendency to coincide with the rotation poles of the earth; this effect, however, is weak and allows deviations between the two sets of poles. It is generally considered that in the present period the deviations have about their maximum value. From data derived from the magnetization of rocks of different periods it follows that the mean positions of both sets of poles during the last few hundred million years have been, indeed, nearly coincident.

Inside the core, at a depth of about 5050 km, a narrow zone of density transition has been found, i.e., from about 4980—5120 km. The part of the core inside this zone is usually known as the inner core. This probably does not take part in the core currents; it is often surmised that it has the character of a solid.

We shall not go deeper into the problems concerning the core; our main subjects are concerned with the crust and mantle, and although the mantle is in direct contact with the core, it is usually considered that the effect of the core on the mantle and the crust is small and probably negligible. One important exception has, however, to be made; the core is a continuous source of heat which no doubt strongly influences the mantle. If, in fact, the core did not lose heat to the mantle, we should not be able to understand the existence of the core currents; in that case the source of instability of the core caused by cooling would not be present and we could not attribute the core currents to temperature convection. This considera-tion is also one of the arguments in favour of convection currents in the mantle. Only by assuming such currents can we explain that the earth's cooling has pene-trated so far down; heat conduction and heat radiation would be insufficient to account for it.

7

The main constituent of the mantle is supposed to be $Fe_2Mg_2SiO_4$. In the upper 500 km of the mantle it occurs as olivine, i.e., in the orthorhombic phase; in the lower 2000 km probably as spinel, i.e., in the cubic phase; and in the transition layer between the depths of 500 and 900 km it is likely to show gradually changing proportions of the two phases. After allowances for the effects of pressure and temperature on the values they have at the earth's surface (BIRCH, 1942), the density of the upper mantle part (olivine form) is about 3.27 g/cm^3 and that of the lower part (spinel form) about 4.00 g/cm^3.

It is difficult to explain the deformations to which the crust is subject, without assuming slow currents in the mantle. There is reason to suppose that these currents have the character of convection currents induced by the cooling of the earth at its surface. Because the mantle is crystalline, these currents must take the form of pseudo-flow. The way the crustal deformations occur, points to velocities of this pseudo-flow of a few cm/year, with maxima of the order of 10 cm/year. So we see that the mantle currents are of the order of a million times slower than the core currents. The fact that the distribution of the crustal deformations is such that we must assume the mantle currents to occur over the full thickness of the mantle, has led to the above-mentioned hypothesis that the lower 2000 km of the mantle has the same chemical composition as the upper 500 km, from which matter reaches the earth's surface in volcanic eruptions. These facts have indicated that olivine and spinel are the main constituents of the mantle.

In the study MEIJERING and ROOYMANS (1958) made of the mantle, they mentioned that the spinel lattice is tolerant to solution and so enstatite ($MgSiO_3$) and other metal ions such as Na, K, Ca, Al, etc. might also be present in the lower 2000 km of the mantle. In the olivine form, in the upper 500 km, solution is more difficult, but here these other constituents may be carried along by the mantle currents. So the constitution of the mantle is probably more complicated than the simple olivine-spinel supposition we started with.

With respect to the thermal conditions in the mantle we may first of all mention the principal fact which dominates the whole history of the earth, the extreme smallness of the thermal conductivity. BIRCH (1942) gives figures of the order of 4—8 · 10^{-3} cal/sec cm deg. The result is that the temperature conduction is slow, even compared with the velocities of the mantle convection currents which are of the order of a few centimetres per year. This brings about the result that the temperature is, roughly speaking, carried along with the particles of the current, and so these particles more or less keep their thermal density deviations.

In Chapter IV, we shall use this result in the study of the mantle convection currents. Together with the elastic limit which the stress deviator in the mantle has to exceed before flow can start, it leads to half-turn currents, whereby the surface matter of the mantle, which loses its heat by radiation towards the outside and, therefore, acquires a higher density than the deeper mantle matter, is brought down, and the matter of higher temperature and lower density is brought up, until dynamic stability is reached and the current stops. According to the geological data about tectonic activity, which is caused by the drag exerted by these currents on the crust, the half-turn mantle currents last about 50—100 million years. According to the seismological and geological evidence we are at present living in the second half of such a half-turn period.

After the half-turn mantle convection current has stopped, a long period of rest follows, during which the upper mantle layer at a high temperature again loses heat by radiation and the lower mantle layer at a relatively low temperature is heated up by the core. After a few hundred million years the original situation of instability in the mantle is restored and a new half-turn current can develop, again causing tectonic activity in the crust. In this way we can explain the episodic recurrence of orogenic periods at the earth's surface.

We shall now deal with the constitution of the crust. In the continents it usually consists of an upper layer of granite, often covered by sediments, and a lower layer which is generally supposed to consist of basalt. In the geosynclinal belts, where the horizontal compression caused by mantle currents has compressed the crust and has caused down-buckling, the above constitution is strongly disturbed, and erosion and sedimentation have further complicated matters. In the belts of crustal tension, i.e., the belts of graben and horsts, the situation is similarly disturbed. In both areas volcanoes have played their part in causing changes in the normal constitution of the crust; great masses of lava may cover or intrude into the crust.

The oceanic crust is less well known than that of the continents. It is usually assumed that under the oceans the mantle matter is covered by a basaltic layer of only some 5—10 km thickness, and on top of that is a layer of sediments which, far from the continents, has a thickness of not more than a few kilometres. Near the mouths of rivers this layer may obviously be much thicker. It is clear that also in the oceans, where volcanic activity may be considerable, great masses of lava may be present, i.e., as volcanic islands, on the sea floor, and also as crustal intrusions. The constitution of the crust in mid-ocean rises is not yet clear. Whether the mantle currents, which probably rise below these ridges, have affected the constitution of the crust is a question which can not yet be finally answered. Seismic velocities often show figures between those of granite and basalt, and they have not yet been clearly interpreted.

Up to now we have dealt with the constitution of the chemical crust, comprising all material that is different from the mantle matter. We shall now examine the rigid crust, which in its behaviour differs from the mantle by reason of greater rigidity. Although it is often carried along by the mantle currents, it does not follow these currents as if it formed a whole with the mantle. As an example we may consider the geosynclinal belts where, by the horizontal compression caused by the mantle currents, the crust locally gives way, while in contrast with this the crust on both sides is deformed only a little.

It is very likely that in the continental areas the rigid crust is more or less identical with the chemical crust. As we shall see in Section III.3, parts of this crust, that by down-buckling are pushed down into the mantle, are swept away by the mantle currents and distributed in a thin layer which over a large area is added to the crust from below. This clearly characterizes a discontinuous change in mobility at that level.

It is questionable whether below the oceans such a discontinuity is present. According to the isostatic equilibrium of great volcanic islands (Hawaii, for example) which we shall deal with in the next Section, the rigid crust in the oceans has at least the same thickness as in the continents, and so it follows that here a considerable layer of olivine must, in addition to the thin chemical crust, form part of the rigid crust. In these areas the temperature obviously plays a dominant part, rendering the surface layer of the olivine more rigid than the olivine lower down.

2. *Isostasy*

Long ago gravity observations and determinations of deflections of the vertical showed that below mountains deficiencies of mass occur which appear to compensate the mass excesses represented by the mountains. This was first noted by BOUGUER (1749) in the area of the Peruvian Andes and by PRATT (1855) and AIRY (1855) in the area south of the Himalaya. For this phenomenon, DUTTON in 1889 proposed the word *isostasy*. The term has since been used everywhere.

AIRY (1855) was the first to give an acceptable physical explanation. He supposed that in general the earth's crust floats on a denser more or less fluid substratum, and that in mountain areas the crust has become thickened by compression. It thus sinks deeper in the fluid sub-stratum and this causes mass deficiencies compensating the mountain masses. Roughly speaking, we can say that in order to keep the pressure the same at a level of, say, 100 km below sea level, the vertical columns above this level must contain the same amount of mass.

Investigating this more closely, we see that this physical principle, which we could describe as isostatic equilibrium, for two reasons involves slight deviations from mass equality between different columns. In the first place the force of gravity slightly increases downwards and so the compensating mass deficiency must be slightly less than the topographical mass for accurately compensating the pressure exerted on a deeper level. In the second place the verticals converge downwards, and this likewise causes the compensating masses to be somewhat less than the topographic masses. Together this means that the compensating mass deficiency in its absolute value may be expected to be a few percent less than the topographical mass (see HEISKANEN and VENING MEINESZ, 1958; VENING MEINESZ, 1946). Isostasy is not so accurately realized, that it is possible to check the presence of these deviations by gravity observations.

That, indeed, isostasy is a tendency towards floating equilibrium of the crust on a plastic mantle and not a mass arrangement somehow brought into being by the way topography originated, is, for example, made likely by the fact that great deltas, such as the Mississippi delta and the Nile delta, show normal gravity. If the equilibrium had no tendency to readjust itself, excesses of gravity ought to be present there. It is likewise confirmed by the fact that the great ice loads of thousands of metres of ice, which were present in Fennoscandia and in the north of North America during the last glacial period, strongly depressed those areas. In the present period these areas are still rising because of the readjustment towards equilibrium. In northern Europe the negative gravity anomalies make it likely that at present about two-thirds of the depression has disappeared and this is in good harmony with the time curve of the uplift, as derived from old shore lines and varves, and from the present rate of rise found by means of tide gauges and marigraphs. In Fennoscandia the maximum rising velocity is 1.1 cm/year; it occurs in Ångermanland.

From these phenomena a formula may be derived for the relaxation period t_r, during which the deviation from equilibrium diminishes to $1/e$ of its initial value. For an elliptical depression of dimension L Mm in one direction and N Mm at right-angles to it, we find:

$$t_r LN \, (L^2 + N^2)^{-\frac{1}{2}} = 6.3 \, Mm \, y_m$$

in which Mm is a megametre, i.e., 1000 km, and y_m a time unit of one thousand years.

In 1923, when the writer succeeded in making gravity observations at sea, at least on broad lines isostatic equilibrium appeared to be present in the oceans. This confirmed the expectations; if it had been otherwise, great problems would have presented themselves.

The way the isostatic compensation is achieved below the topography depends on how this topography came into being. For a volcanic island it is in general regionally spread out over an area of a few hundred kilometres greater breadth than the island. From this we can conclude that the crust is bending down elastically under the weight of the island. This is the case for Hawaii and Madeira, for example. For the Azores it is somewhat different; probably these islands are mainly formed by volcanic activity along great crustal fault planes in an azimuth of about N55°W, and this would lead to a tendency towards regional compensation in that direction and local compensation at right-angles to it. The gravity results seem, indeed, to support this conclusion.

For the topography formed by the transition from the continents to the deep sea, we must expect local compensation corresponding to the shape of the edge of the sialic continental block. This is confirmed by gravity measurements over these areas.

Gravimetric cross-sections over a folded mountain range must be expected to reveal the presence of a relatively narrow root of light crustal matter formed by the crustal down-buckling along the geosyncline of the range. This represents the isostatic compensation of this mountain range. The gravimetric survey over the Swiss Alps has confirmed this surmise. In the area of the western Alps, the root is found under the highest range, to the south of the Rhône valley.

The means for carrying out this research are provided by tables allowing a relatively easy reduction of the results of a gravimetric survey for the effects of the Newton attraction by the topographic masses and by the isostatic compensation masses corresponding to that topography. If after this reduction the gravity anomalies no longer show a correlation with the topography, we may conclude that probably, although not necessarily, the topography is, indeed, isostatically compensated in the way supposed in the making of the tables. For local isostatic compensation and different thicknesses of the undisturbed crust, Heiskanen and his collaborators have prepared the tables (HEISKANEN, 1938). For regional compensation corresponding to different degrees of regionality the writer has done the same. By applying the different tables we can find out which manner of compensation is likely to be nearest to the truth. A complete proof is not obtained; since an infinity of mass distributions provide the same field of attraction at the earth's surface no such proof is possible. The conclusion is, however, likely to be sound.

We do not wish here to go deeply into the problems of these topographic and isostatic reductions. Two points, however, may be mentioned. In the first place it may be remarked that for taking into account the attraction effects of topographical and compensation masses, a system of circular zones around the station in question is introduced, spreading over the whole earth's surface; for this purpose usually the system taken is that introduced by HAYFORD and BOWIE (1912). In the neighbourhood of the station the zones are only a few metres broad, but at great distances they spread over large areas of the earth's surface.

The second point to be mentioned is, that taking away the effects of the topographical and compensation masses has to be accompanied by removing an indirect effect brought about by the change of potential of the earth which attends this taking away of masses (VENING MEINESZ, 1946). The indirect reduction amounts to only a few milligals; it is usually neglected.

Also in areas where large gravity anomalies occur, it is important, in order to be able to interpret these anomalies, first to take off the effects of topography and isostatic compensation. By means of the tables mentioned this can easily be done. Only after applying these reductions can we get an idea about the deviations from equilibrium in the earth which the anomalies represent, and obtain indications

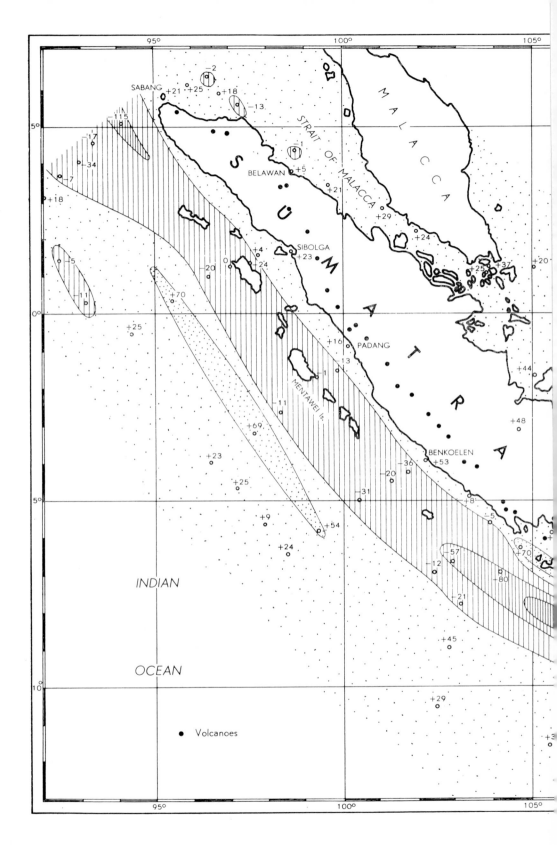

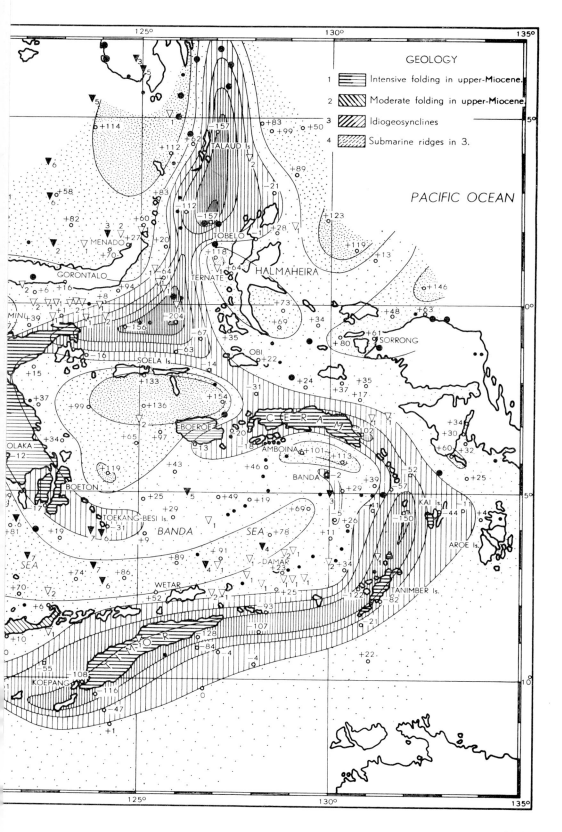

GEOLOGY

1 ▭ Intensive folding in upper-Miocene.

2 ▧ Moderate folding in upper-Miocene.

3 ▨ Idiogeosynclines

4 ▨ Submarine ridges in 3.

PACIFIC OCEAN

pp. 19-24

about the forces working in the earth and causing these deviations. As an example reference is made to Fig.II.1 and 2, which give the gravity anomalies in the Indonesian archipelago, i.e., Fig.II.1, after topographical and local isostatic reduction, and Fig.II.2, after topographical and regional isostatic reduction. On both maps we see a belt of strong negative anomalies, but on the first map it is much more irregular than on the second. We thus see how important these reductions are for obtaining a good idea about the deviations from equilibrium occurring in the earth and about the forces working.

In this case we see that in the Indonesian archipelago a linear belt occurs where the earth's crust is depressed below its equilibrium position. In Section III.2, we shall discuss this belt and we shall find that probably the crust is down-buckling here under the effect of strong uniaxial horizontal compression; we may conclude that this phenomenon represents a geosyncline in the making.

3. The equilibrium figure of the earth and the geodetic problem of deriving the figure of the earth from gravity

For our geophysical study of the processes working in the earth, it is important to know what the equilibrium figure and the gravity field of the earth would be in the absence of these processes. This, therefore, is the figure the earth would adopt under the effect of the mutual Newton attraction of all its particles and of its rotation, and its gravity field under these conditions. This would make it possible to consider the deviation of the real gravity field from this equilibrium field as the effect caused by the forces working in the earth.

We thus have found a common problem, or a series of common problems, with geodesy. If the geodesist adopted the equilibrium figure of the earth as its surface of reference, and if his formula for normal gravity corresponded to this reference surface, the gravity anomalies and the deflections of the vertical would have the important meaning of being caused by the same forces working in the earth that are the subject of this study.

It is likely that notwithstanding the crystalline character of the mantle and the presence of disturbances in it the earth has closely approached equilibrium. This view follows from the general tendency towards isostasy which can only be interpreted as a tendency towards floating equilibrium of the rigid crust on the mantle.

If the density of the earth were uniform the problem of the equilibrium figure would be simple. It would be a rotation ellipsoid with a flattening depending on the velocity of rotation. The density, however, increases considerably downwards, probably up to about 12 g/cm³ in the centre, and this renders the problem of its equilibrium figure more complicated. Many scientists have occupied themselves with it; we may mention CLAIRAUT (1743), TISSERAND (1891), DARWIN (1899), VÉRONNET (1912), DE SITTER (1924), and BULLARD (1948). The density increase mentioned, in so far as it is caused by compression, is more or less continuous; however, in the transition layer between the depths of 500 and 900 km there is a much more rapid increase than elsewhere, which is caused by the change of the mantle matter in another modification. Besides, the density changes discontinuously at a number of discontinuity surfaces, viz. several in the crust, one between crust and mantle, one between mantle and core and one between outer and inner core. We shall not enlarge on the complicated problem of deriving the equilibrium figure, but only mention the result.

If we are satisfied with an accuracy in the radius of 1 m we can say that the equilibrium figure is a rotation spheroid of which the deviation from the rotation ellipsoid is remarkably small. If we choose the ellipsoid in such a way that it coincides with the equilibrium spheroid at the equator and poles, the spheroid has a maximum depression at 45° of northern and southern latitude of 4.3 m. For most cases we can neglect this small difference and adopt as equilibrium figure the ellipsoid used by geodesists.

In general the radius of the earth spheroid can be given by the formula:

$$r = a \left(1 - a \sin^2 B + \alpha_4 \sin^2 2B\right)$$

in which B is the latitude, α the flattening, given by the formula $(a-b)/a$, where a is the equatorial radius and b the polar radius, and α_4 a small quantity of the order of magnitude of α^2, which for the geodesist's earth ellipsoid may be put at 0.0000071.

From the formula for r we can derive the following formula for the gravity γ along the meridian of the earth spheroid:

$$\gamma = \gamma_e \left(1 + \beta \sin^2 B - \beta_4 \sin^2 2B\right)$$

in which γ_e is the value of normal gravity at the equator and β a constant, which, by means of the theorem of Clairaut, can be derived from the flattening. Up to the order of the first power of the flattening, this theorem gives:

$$a + \beta = \frac{5}{2} c$$

in which c is the ratio of the centrifugal acceleration at the equator divided by the gravity at the equator; β_4 is a small quantity of the order of magnitude of α^2 which for the geodesist's earth ellipsoid may be put at 0.0000059.

Introducing the other figures adopted in geodesy, these two formulae become:

$$r = 6,378,388 \left(1 - 0.0033670 \sin^2 B + 0.0000071 \sin^2 2B\right) \text{ m}$$
$$\gamma = 978,049 \left(1 + 0.0052884 \sin^2 B - 0.0000059 \sin^2 2B\right) \text{ gal}$$

According to the latest satellite data, which must be considered to be more accurate than the geodetic data, the flattening would be 1/228 part smaller than the value of 1/297.0 used for the above formulae; it should be 1/298.3.

As has been mentioned the real earth is not accurately in equilibrium, and as a consequence of this, gravity differs from the values given by the above formula for normal gravity; the deviations rarely come up to values of 200 mgal. These deviations correspond to deviations of the geoid, which is the equipotential surface of the earth at mean sea level, i.e., the surface of the seas, if not disturbed by winds, currents or tides, which as "sea level" can be determined by precise levelling in the land areas. The distance between the geoid and reference ellipsoid is usually less than 40 m above or below. This distance, which in geodesy is usually indicated by the letter N, can be determined by means of gravity determinations. In 1849, STOKES published a theorem giving a relation between this distance N and the gravity anomalies, which are the deviations of gravity, reduced to sea level, from the normal value of gravity as given by the above formula. However, for one value of N we need in theory the gravity anomalies over the whole earth. Because gravity is not known everywhere, this must, for a long time, present an unsurmountable difficulty. In practice, however, the effect in the formula of Stokes' theorem of distant gravity anomalies is so small that we can neglect it. Still it is necessary to have a detailed knowledge of the anomalies up to at least a distance of about 50 km, and a more general knowledge of them up to about 1000 km. These facts reduce the applicability of the method for determining the figure of the earth.

We shall not go deeply into these geodetic problems, but it is worth while to realize that in these problems we deal with the deviations from equilibrium in the earth which are so important for the geophysicists. We shall, therefore, in the next Section briefly investigate the external gravity field of the earth, which affects flying missiles. In this way we can find out whether from observation of their tracks we can obtain valuable information on geophysical problems. It is, however, impossible to carry this out without mathematical deductions, and so we shall have to make an exception in this Section to the general line followed in this book. The reader who does not want to study these deductions may be referred to the conclusions arrived at and mentioned at the end of the Section.

4. *The external gravity field of the earth*[1]

Flying missiles have suddenly increased the importance of knowing the gravity field of the earth up to great distances. Although the writer formerly published formulae about this matter (HEISKANEN and VENING MEINESZ, 1958, formulae 3-3, 4, 5, 6 and 9), it may at present be useful to go into more detail.

We start from the formula for the outside potential of a spheroidal earth; the coordinates used are the radius r to the earth's centre of gravity and the geocentric latitude φ. We shall assume that the outside point where we investigate the poten-

---

[1] This is a slightly modified republication of an earlier paper (VENING MEINESZ, 1959).

tial is not rotating round the earth's axis. Up to the fourth order term, i.e., up to the second order of the earth's flattening, we have:

$$U = k\frac{M}{r}\left[1 - \frac{C}{Mr^2}H\left(\frac{3}{2}\sin^2\varphi - \frac{1}{2}\right) + \frac{D}{r^4}\left(\sin^4\varphi - \frac{6}{7}\sin^2\varphi + \frac{3}{35}\right) \cdots\right] \qquad (1)$$

where k is Newton's constant, M the mass of the earth, C the moment of inertia round the rotation-axis, H the "mechanical ellipticity", i.e., the ratio $(C—A)/C$, in which A is the moment of inertia round an axis in the equatorial plane, and finally, D a higher order moment of inertia divided by M, given by:

$$D = \frac{1}{M}\int_0^M \frac{1225}{64} r^4\left(\sin^4\varphi - \frac{6}{7}\sin^2\varphi + \frac{3}{35}\right) dm \qquad (2)$$

We know that, because of its rotation, the earth in its general shape assumed the figure of a flattened spheroid, and research by CLAIRAUT (1743), DARWIN (1899), DE SITTER (1924), and others have shown that the equilibrium figure of a rotating fluid body of the same volume, mass and general density distribution as the earth is a spheroid closely approaching a rotation ellipsoid; both surfaces do not deviate from each other more than about two metres. It is clear, therefore, that the geodesists, in taking a flattened ellipsoid as reference figure for the earth, are near to the true figure.

Examining our problem now in greater detail, and taking for the figure of the earth the geoid, which is the equipotential surface of the earth (therefore everywhere at right-angles to gravity) at mean sea-level, we find that the real earth deviates in three ways from the rotation ellipsoid; all three, however, only slightly affect the gravity field at great distances from the earth. In the first place the equilibrium spheroid is not exactly the rotation ellipsoid. In the second place the geoid is not precisely coinciding with the equilibrium spheroid. In the third place the real surface of the earth's masses shows topography and, therefore, does not coincide with the geoid. In these masses we obviously have to include the water masses at the earth's surface; we can, however, show that the masses of the atmosphere are too small to affect our problem appreciably.

Of the three deviations mentioned the first is evidently likewise negligible. For the third this is also true, since the rigid crust of the earth, of a thickness of about 35 km, is floating on the heavier and plastic sub-crustal layer, the masses of the topography are, therefore, compensated by masses of opposite sign lower down. This phenomenon, called isostasy, makes for the total mass in every vertical column of the same horizontal cross-section and down to the same depth being about the same over the whole earth's surface. The differences in location of the masses in each column are too small to affect appreciably the outside gravity field at greater elevation than some fifty kilometres. Near the continental coasts, which constitute the largest topographic features at the earth's surface, we have perhaps to increase this limit up to a height of 100—200 km, but the deviations in figure of the equipotential surfaces and in gravity are local and average out over a belt along the coasts of a few hundred kilometres broad.

The largest deviations are caused by the second of the three causes mentioned above. The masses of the earth appear to deviate sufficiently from the regular layering, which would correspond to fluid equilibrium, to cause the geoid to deviate from the equilibrium spheroid over horizontal distances up to one thousand kilometres or more and over vertical distances up to 40 m. Similar deviations must be present in outside equipotential surfaces and we shall have to study the vertical distances above the earth's surface at which they become negligible. We shall take this up at the end of this Section. Compared to the dimensions of the earth as a whole they are of limited extent.

Replacing the equilibrium spheroid by a rotation ellipsoid of an equatorial radius a and a flattening α, we can derive that for this purpose we have to put:

$$\frac{D}{a^4} = \alpha \left(\frac{7}{2}\alpha - \frac{5}{2}c'\right) \tag{3}$$

where c' is a coefficient dependent on the velocity w of rotation of the earth in the way given by:

$$c' = \frac{w^2 a^3}{kM} \tag{4}$$

It can likewise be shown that the coefficient before the brackets of the second term between the square brackets of formula (1), which as a factor contains the "mechanical ellipticity" as a factor H, is a function of the flattening α and the coefficient c' in the way given by:

$$\frac{CH}{Mr^2} = \frac{CH}{Ma^2} \cdot \frac{a^2}{r^2} = \frac{1}{3}\left(2\alpha - c' - 2\alpha^2 + 2\alpha c' + \frac{2}{7}\frac{D}{a^4}\right)\frac{a^2}{r^2} =$$
$$= \frac{1}{3}\left(2\alpha - c' - \alpha^2 + \frac{9}{7}\alpha c'\right)\frac{a^2}{r^2} \tag{5}$$

Our formula (1) now gives for the outside potential of an ellipsoidal earth at a point at a distance r from the earth's centre and a geocentral latitude φ:

$$U = k\frac{M}{r}\left[1 - \frac{1}{3}\left(2\alpha - c' - \alpha^2 + \frac{9}{7}\alpha c'\right)\frac{a^2}{r^2}\left(\frac{2}{3}\sin^2\varphi - \frac{1}{2}\right) + \right.$$
$$\left. + \left(\frac{7}{2}\alpha^2 - \frac{5}{2}\alpha c'\right)\frac{a^4}{r^4}\left(\sin^4\varphi - \frac{6}{7}\sin^2\varphi + \frac{3}{35}\right)\cdots\right] \tag{6}$$

In order to make this formula complete for the rotating earth, we have to add the potential of the centrifugal force, which is given by:

$$U_r = \tfrac{1}{2} w^2 r^2 \cos^2 \varphi \tag{7}$$

In this formula w is the velocity of rotation; it can easily be computed.

The radius r_e of an arbitrary point of the earth ellipsoid, which has a great axis $2a$ and a flattening α, is up to the second order of α given by:

$$r_e = a \left[1 - \left(\alpha + \tfrac{3}{2} \alpha^2 \right) \sin^2 \varphi + \tfrac{3}{2} \alpha^2 \sin^4 \varphi \ldots \right] \tag{8}$$

Because the earth ellipsoid is supposed to be an equipotential surface of the rotating earth, this value of r_e, introduced in the sum $U + U_r$ must give a result that is independent on the geocentric latitude φ. This condition provides us with the equations (3) and (5) already mentioned.

We shall now use our formula (6) for the earth's gravity field for points not rotating with the earth. The formula for the radius of equipotential surfaces of this field must have the character of the radius of a spheroid up to the second order of their flattening. We shall indicate this radius by ϱ and the equatorial radius of an external equipotential surface by a_ϱ; we shall give the same sub-index to the flattening and to the corresponding 4th order term. We write, therefore, for the radius of the external equipotential spheroid:

$$\varrho = a_\varrho \left[1 - (\alpha_\varrho + \alpha_{\varrho 4}) \sin^2 \varphi + \alpha_{\varrho 4} \sin^4 \varphi \right] \tag{9}$$

Introducing this value of r in equation (6) we obtain two equations expressing that the value of U must be independent of φ; the coefficients of $\sin^2 \varphi$ and $\sin^4 \varphi$ must, therefore, vanish. This gives us:

$$\alpha_\varrho = \frac{1}{2} \left(2\alpha - c' - \alpha^2 + \frac{9}{7} \alpha c' \right) \frac{a^2}{a_\varrho^2} - \frac{1}{2} \left(-\alpha^2 + \frac{9}{7} \alpha c' - \frac{1}{2} c'^2 \right) \frac{a^4}{a_\varrho^4} \tag{10a}$$

$$\alpha_{\varrho 4} = \frac{1}{2} (3\alpha^2 - \alpha c' - c'^2) \frac{a^4}{a_\varrho^4} \tag{10b}$$

From formula (10a) we can draw the conclusion that the first term of the flattening α_ϱ, which forms by far its main part, is inversely proportional to the square of the distance a_ϱ from the earth's centre to the equator of the equipotential surface. We could also have drawn this conclusion from the fact that the flattening constitutes a second order spherical harmonic of the earth's gravity potential, divided by gravity (inversely proportional to a_ϱ^2) and by a_ϱ; the second order spherical harmonic of the gravity potential itself must be inversely proportional to a_ϱ^3.

For α and c' we may now introduce the values for the internationally adopted earth ellipsoid:

$$\alpha = 0.0033670 = 1/297.00 \qquad c' = 0.0034614 \tag{11}$$

30

We thus obtain:

$$\frac{\alpha_\varrho}{\alpha} = 0.48654\,\frac{a^2}{a_\varrho^2} + 0.00035\,\frac{a^4}{a_\varrho^4} \tag{12}$$

which shows that the 4th order term is practically negligible. We, therefore, can state that the flattening is inversely proportional to the square of the equatorial radius of the equipotential spheroid. We get the following values:

$$
\begin{array}{lcccc}
\dfrac{a_\varrho}{a} = & 1 & 2 & 3 & 10 \\[2mm]
\dfrac{\alpha_\varrho}{\alpha} = & 0.48688 & 0.12166 & 0.05406 & 0.00487
\end{array}
\tag{13}
$$

We see that the suppression of the rotation makes the equipotential spheroid with the same equator as the earth ellipsoid have about half of the flattening of the earth ellipsoid. We also see the quick decrease of the flattening with the distance.

We shall now turn to the outside gravity field itself. Differentiation of U (formula 6) with respect to r gives us the gravity component g_r in the direction of this radius and with respect to φ the much smaller gravity component g_S in the south direction at right angles to the radius. We obtain:

$$g_r = -\frac{\delta U}{\delta r} = k\,\frac{M}{r^2}\Bigg[1 - \Big(2\alpha - c' - \alpha^2 + \frac{9}{7}\,\alpha c'\Big)\frac{a^2}{r^2}\Big(\frac{3}{2}\sin^2\varphi - \frac{1}{2}\Big) +$$
$$+\ 5\Big(\frac{7}{2}\alpha^2 - \frac{5}{2}\,\alpha c'\Big)\frac{a^4}{r^4}\Big(\sin^4\varphi - \frac{6}{7}\sin^2\varphi + \frac{3}{35}\Big)\Bigg] \tag{14a}$$

$$g_S = -\frac{\delta U}{r\,\delta\varphi} = k\,\frac{M}{r^2}(2\alpha - c')\frac{a^2}{r^2}\sin\varphi\cos\varphi \tag{14b}$$

As, obviously, the effect of the south component g_S on the total value of gravity is of the order of magnitude of the flattening, we have not derived the formula for g_S farther than up to the first order of α. Under these circumstances we can determine the resultant of both components by means of the formula:

$$g = g_r\Bigg[1 + \frac{1}{2}\Big(\frac{g_S}{g_r}\Big)^2\Bigg] \tag{15}$$

and obtain for g an accuracy up to the second order of the flattening; by replacing $\sin^2\varphi\cos^2\varphi$ by $\sin^2\varphi - \sin^4\varphi$ we get:

$$g = k\,\frac{M}{r^2}\Bigg[1 - \Big(2\alpha - c' - \alpha^2 + \frac{9}{7}\,\alpha c'\Big)\frac{a^2}{r^2}\Big(\frac{3}{2}\sin^2\varphi - \frac{1}{2}\Big) +$$
$$+\ 5\Big(\frac{7}{2}\alpha^2 - \frac{5}{2}\,\alpha c'\Big)\frac{a^4}{r^4}\Big(\sin^4\varphi - \frac{6}{7}\sin^2\varphi + \frac{3}{35}\Big) + \frac{1}{2}(2\alpha - c')^2\frac{a^4}{r^4}(\sin^2\varphi - \sin^4\varphi)\Bigg] \tag{16}$$

By dividing g_S by g_r we can obtain the tangent of the angle Θ between the direction of gravity and the geocentric radius r and because this angle is of the order of the flattening, we can replace the tangent by the angle itself. By multiplying the ratio by ϱ'' we obtain this angle in seconds of arc. We find:

$$\Theta'' = \varrho'' \, (2\alpha - c') \frac{a^2}{r^2} \sin \varphi \cos \varphi \left[1 + (2\alpha - c') \frac{a^2}{r^2} \left(\frac{3}{2} \sin^2 \varphi - \frac{1}{2} \right) \right] \tag{17}$$

Introducing the values of α and c' of the earth, the formulae (16) and (17) become:

$$\left. \begin{aligned} g &= k \frac{M}{r^2} \left[1 - 0.972 \; \alpha \frac{a^2}{r^2} \left(\frac{3}{2} \sin^2 \varphi - \frac{1}{2} \right) + \right. \\ &\left. + 4.650 \; \alpha^2 \frac{a^4}{r^4} \left(\sin^4 \varphi - \frac{6}{7} \sin^2 \varphi + \frac{3}{35} \right) + 0.472 \; \alpha^2 \frac{a^4}{r^4} (\sin^2 \varphi - \sin^4 \varphi) \right] \end{aligned} \right\} \tag{16a}$$

$$\Theta'' = 198420'' \; \alpha \frac{a^2}{r^2} \sin \varphi \cos \varphi \left[1 + 0.972 \; \alpha \frac{a^2}{r^2} \left(\frac{3}{2} \sin^2 \varphi - \frac{1}{2} \right) \right] \tag{17a}$$

For obtaining the direction of gravity the angle Θ has to be added to φ. We thus have derived gravity outside the earth in magnitude and direction.

We shall now take up the problem of how we can determine the relatively slight deviations in the equipotential surfaces and in gravity caused by the disturbing masses which bring about the gravity anomalies and the deviations between earth ellipsoid and geoid. Their effect is limited compared to what has hitherto been considered. It is, therefore, only appreciable up to small distances outside the geoid.

We apply STOKES' (1849) method, adapted to this case, and consider the undisturbed equipotential surfaces at geoid level and at an arbitrary distance outside it as spheres with radii a and a_ϱ. We shall denote the gravity anomalies on these surfaces by δg and δg_ϱ and the distances between the disturbed and the undisturbed surfaces by N and N_ϱ. Denoting a/a_ϱ by u we have $u \leq 1$. By means of Stokes's method we can write:

$$N = \frac{a}{4\pi g \, a_\varrho^2} \int_o^{S=4\pi a^2} F_\varrho \delta g \; dS \tag{18a}$$

with:

$$F_\varrho = \frac{2}{uv} + \frac{1}{u} - 5 \cos \psi - 3 \frac{v}{u} - 3 \cos \psi \ln \tfrac{1}{2} (1 - u \cos \psi + v) \tag{18b}$$

where:

$$v = (1 - 2u \cos \psi + u^2)^{\frac{1}{2}} \tag{18c}$$

These formulae give us the disturbance in the outside equipotential surfaces caused by the disturbing masses in the earth which cause the gravity anomalies.

For deriving the gravity anomalies on these outside equipotential surfaces, we can write:

$$\delta g_\varrho = \frac{1}{4\pi a^2} \int_{\varrho}^{S=4\pi a^2} \delta g \left[\sum_{n=0}^{n=\infty} (2n+1) \, P_n u^{n+2} \right] dS \qquad (19)$$

In the following way we can derive the quantity between the square brackets and obtain the solution:

$$G_\varrho = \sum_{n=2}^{n=\infty} (2n+1) \, P_n u^{n+2} = 2u^{2\frac{1}{2}} \sum_{2}^{\infty} (n+\tfrac{1}{2}) \, P_n u^{n-\frac{1}{2}} = 2u^{2\frac{1}{2}} \frac{d}{du} \left(\sum_{2}^{\infty} P_n u^{n+\frac{1}{2}} \right)$$

This gives:

$$G_\varrho = 2 \, u^{2\frac{1}{2}} \frac{d}{du} \left(u^{\frac{1}{2}} \, q \right) \qquad (20a)$$

where:

$$q = \sum_{2}^{\infty} P_n u^n = (1 - 2 \, u \cos \psi + u^2)^{-\frac{1}{2}} - 1 - u \cos \psi \qquad (20b)$$

We thus obtain the solution (19) in the form:

$$\delta g_\varrho = \frac{1}{4\pi a^2} \int_{\varrho}^{S=4\pi a^2} G_\varrho \delta g dS \qquad (20c)$$

Although we thus can derive the outside equipotential surfaces and the gravity field, this solution does not provide us with a quick insight in the distance from the earth's surface up to which the earth's disturbing masses have an appreciable effect. We can solve this problem better by making use of the fact that we can represent the outside gravity anomalies corresponding to anomalies on the geoid distributed according to a spherical harmonic Y_n of order n by the formula $Y_n u^{n+2}$. We thus can derive that the gravity anomalies sink to about one percent at an elevation of $30.000/n + 2$ km. For the belts of strong negative anomalies in island-arc areas, as, for example, in the areas of the Indonesian and Caribbean archipelagos, this is the case for elevations of 200—250 km. This is a good illustration of the relatively small distances from the earth to which the effect of disturbing masses in the earth is limited.

It follows from these results that from the satellite observations we can not expect contributions towards the discovery of local gravity anomaly features, such as the belts of strong negative anomalies, which are so important for our investigations. They may, however, provide us with other contributions of great value. They may reveal larger fields of anomalies pointing to deviations from equilibrium in the

33

mantle which may be connected with mantle currents. And they have already given data of primary importance, to geodesists as well as to geophysicists, about the flattening of the earth. This in itself is a result of the highest importance. For the geophysicist it has the great value of liberating the gravity anomalies from the consequences of a wrong formula for normal gravity. The value of α found in this way is $1/298.3 = 0.0033524$ and according to the theorem of Clairaut the value of β must be 0.0053030. Up to now these new values for α and β have not yet been introduced in the formulae for r and γ.

5. *Active volcanicity a cause of deviations from equilibrium*

It is likely that the presence of active volcanoes in some areas leads to a deviation from equilibrium in those areas. The rising volcanic matter, on which the pressure is relieved, is obviously subject to more or less explosive gas release, leading to an upward movement. This must bring about a gravity excess and, corresponding to that, a rise of the geoid above the equilibrium surface. Both represent deviations from the earth's equilibrium.

The pressure developed must no doubt also work downwards and this must eventually lead to a subsidence of the whole area until isostatic equilibrium has been regained, but this must evidently be a much slower process than that of the rise of volcanic matter. So we may expect that so long as volcanic action is going on, the isostatic equilibrium of the area will be disturbed.

In two volcanic areas the writer has found this conclusion confirmed. In the Indonesian archipelago and in the Azores area he found excesses of gravity, which in both areas amounted to about $+ 30$ mgal. It is true that in the first of these areas we must assume that strong uniaxial compression is present in the crust, and as we shall see in Section III.1, this must lead to an arching effect causing a lifting up of the crust and a corresponding excess of matter, but this cannot lead to a gravity anomaly of more than about 7—9 mgal. So in the Indonesian archipelago a mean positive gravity anomaly of more than 20 mgal has still to be accounted for.

The Indonesian archipelago covers an area of about 6 Mm^2 (1 Mm = one Megametre $= 10^6$ m) and the Azores area about 1 Mm^2; hence both areas are much too large for the strength of the rigid crust to be able to carry extra loads which could explain the mass excesses. The stresses to which the crust is subjected have a quite different character in these two areas; in the Indonesian archipelago we must assume a field of strong uniaxial horizontal compression and in the Azores area a field of horizontal tension. So we cannot find an explanation in this direction. But both areas have one feature in common: they are both strongly volcanic, and this volcanicity is in both cases active. So all the indications are favourable for the hypothesis dealt with in this Section, according to which active volcanicity has a tendency to lead to mass excesses and to systematic positive gravity anomalies.

Chapter III

CRUSTAL PHENOMENA AND DEFORMATIONS

1. *General effect of horizontal compression in the crust*

If the crust is subject to uniaxial compression, the curvature of the crust causes an arching effect; the curved crust is held by the compression in a somewhat higher position than it would occupy without compression. This would obviously be accompanied by a mass excess corresponding to a positive anomaly. For a rise h and for an anomaly A we obtain the following formulae in which σ is the compressional stress in kg/cm² and T the thickness of the rigid crust in km:

$$h = 4.9 \cdot 10^{-4} \sigma T \text{ m}$$
$$A = 6.7 \cdot 10^{-5} \sigma T \text{ mgal}$$

For a crustal thickness of 35 km and a compression of 1000 kg/cm² we obtain a rise h of 17 m and an anomaly of 2.3 mgal. We see that the effect is not large, but that it is not negligible. We shall presently suppose a compression that exceeds the elastic limit of the crust, and such a stress may well amount to 2000 kg/cm². This would give double the amounts mentioned.

Obviously the presence of a second horizontal compressional stress at right-angles to the first would further increase the rise and the anomaly.

2. *Plastic down-buckling of the crust; the origin of geosynclines*

If the crust is subject to uniaxial horizontal compression that exceeds the elastic limit of the crustal matter, we get a much more important crustal process, which leads to the formation of a geosyncline. As BIJLAARD (1935) has shown, plastic deformation of a thin plate subject to uniaxial stress – of course the crust may be considered to satisfy such conditions – occurs in belts making angles of about 55° with the stress direction. The compression can thus lead to the formation of the central part of an island arc, which roughly speaking consists of two parts enclosing an angle of about 110°, which is bisected by the direction of compression. Each part is slightly curved and this also can be explained by Bijlaard's theory; the angle is, therefore, somewhat larger than 110°.

The crustal deformation in these belts starts with a thickening of the crust, but because of isostasy, the lower crustal bulge which forms is much larger than the upper bulge. This causes the median plane in the crust, which, if the crust consists of a granite layer and a basaltic layer of equal thickness, coincides with the bound-

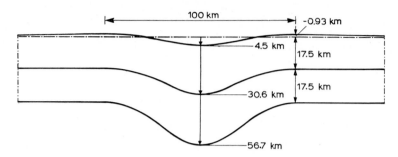

Fig.III.1. Plastic crustal downbuckling of oceanic crust on true vertical scale: upper and lower crustal boundaries and axis plane ($T = 15.6 \cdot 10^6$ years).

ary plane between the two layers, to bend downwards over the whole length of the belt. It is simple to see that this must lead to a down-buckling of the crustal belt under the effect of the strong horizontal compression. A stage of this deformation is shown by Fig.III.1, which gives a cross-section of the belt. It is clear that the central area of the crustal belt is pressed down below its equilibrium level, and this explains the belt of strong negative gravity anomalies occurring in the Indonesian archipelago and in other island-arc areas. The belt is clearly shown by the maps of Fig.II.1 and 2. Interesting experiments, giving a clear representation of this plastic down-buckling of the crust, have been made by KUENEN (1936), who submitted a layer of wax and paraffin floating on water to horizontal compression; the experiments show the down-buckling of this layer (see Fig.III.2).

It is clear that in this crustal phenomenon we have found the way of formation of a geosyncline (HEISKANEN and VENING MEINESZ, 1958, Chapter 10A; VENING MEINESZ, 1955); the geological history of geosynclines, indeed, agrees remarkably well with the details of this crustal process. We can now understand the cause of the subsidence of the crust's surface in these belts during the first stage of the geosyncline formation, and also the gradual laying down of sediments in the belts showing ridge formation and eventually overthrusting.

If the geosyncline is far away from islands or coasts that can provide sediments, the down-buckled belt shows at the surface as a deep trench. Instances of this are found in the Pacific at great distances from Asia, as for example, the Palau, West Caroline and Marianas Trenches.

From the presence of the belts of strong negative anomalies and of the trenches in the island-arc areas we can conclude that we are still living in a period of mantle currents which keep the earth's crust under compressional stress, at least in large areas. If this were not the case these features would disappear. We shall deal with this in the next Section. The presence of great stresses in the crust is also shown by the earthquakes, which accompany the crustal movements caused by these stresses.

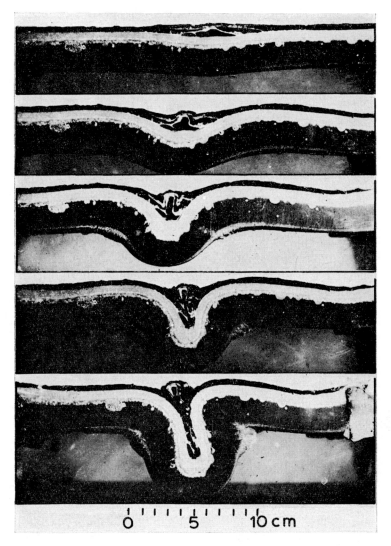

Fig.III.2. Five successive stages of Kuenen's experiments on buckling of a floating plastic layer under uniaxial horizontal compression.

3. *Further history of the geosynclinal areas and their forelands*

When the half-turn convection currents in the mantle have completed their half turn and the mantle is again stable, the stresses in the crust disappear. This has far-reaching consequences for the geosynclinal belts. The great deviation from isostatic equilibrium in those down-pressed belts leads to a readjustment of the crustal equilibrium, which means a considerable rising of these belts. As we saw

37

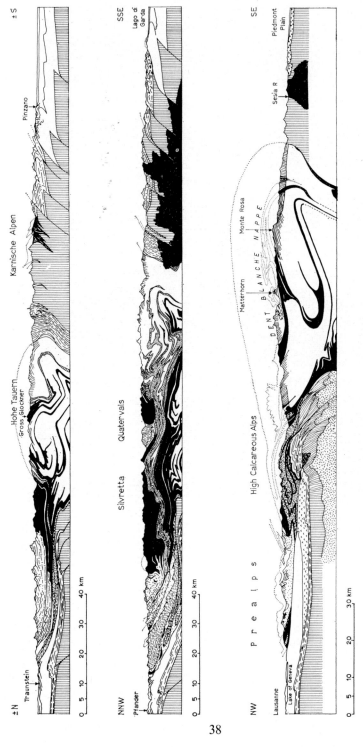

Fig.III.3. Profiles through the Alps. (After BROUWER, 1927, p. 90).

in the preceding Section, the crust has been thickened by the compression. In Fig.III.1, this thickening has been supposed to be 1.49 times, and this stage led to a trench at the crust's surface of a depth of about 4.5 km with regard to the undeformed crust. If this belt readjusts its isostatic equilibrium, this would lead to a mountain belt with an elevation of about 2.3 km. In reality, however, we must assume that usually the geosyncline was filled by sediments, and that, therefore, the mountain range formed would have a mean elevation of the central belt of about 2.8 km, of which the upper 4.5 km would consist of sediments. This is no doubt a simplified picture, because the belt was subjected to great folding and overthrusting, and this must show itself by much folding and deformation of the sediments, and by a more irregular cross-section.

As an example of this we give, in Fig.III.3, three profiles across the Alps, one being by ARGAND (1916) over the Hohe Tauern, and two by STAUB (1924) over the Silvretta, and over the Matterhorn and Monte Rosa. It is remarkable that in all three profiles we see evidence confirming the hypothesis of crustal down-buckling, although all three were published long before the writer had put forward that hypothesis. Since in the Alps the isostatic equilibrium has readjusted itself, and has led to the coming into being of the high mountain ranges, erosion has already attacked the higher parts, and this can be seen in all the three profiles.

The Indonesian archipelago has obviously not yet reached this stage. The belt of negative anomalies must still be held far below its equilibrium position by crustal compression. Only in the high island of Timor, where the highest mountain, Fatamailau, attains an elevation of 2920 m, has the isostatic equilibrium readjusted itself, at least on great lines.

The writer thinks that we can expect that this isostatic readjustment does not operate over the whole length of the down-buckled belt at the same time. The tendency towards readjustment is no doubt present throughout the whole belt, but secondary circumstances will determine where it will be possible for the crustal belt to break free from the surrounding matter, as is needed for rising. There is no doubt that for such a process a strong decrease, if not a complete disappearance, of the uniaxial compression in the crust must take place. This will probably mean that the half-turn current is close to stopping. At an earlier date this must have happened in the Alpine area.

Although in Indonesia it is likely to be near to stopping, that has certainly not yet happened. In 1895, MULLER, chief of the triangulation service, re-measured the triangulation of the Tapanuli area in Sumatra after an earthquake took place, and found shifts of the stations, which pointed to a shockwise relative horizontal movement of the dextral type of about 2.20 m along a fault plane parallel to the axis of Sumatra. The frequency of earthquakes throughout the whole archipelago points in the same direction.

As a consequence of the crustal down-buckling in a geosynclinal belt, another

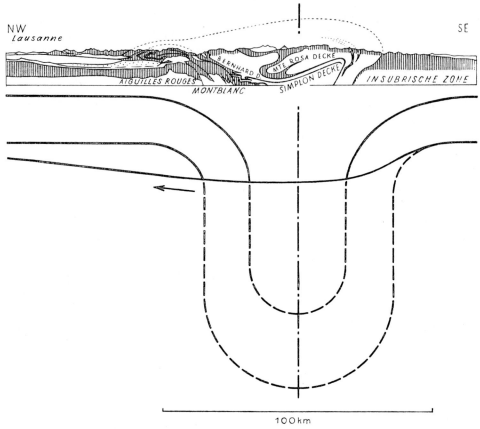

NW
lausanne

SE

AIGUILLES ROUGES
BERNHARD D
MTE ROSA DECKE
SIMPLON DECKE
INSUBRISCHE ZONE
MONTBLANC

100 km

Fig.III.4. The melting and flowing away of the down-buckled root of the Alps. (Alpine profile after STAUB, 1924).

important phenomenon must take place. The down-buckled crustal matter must gradually assume the higher temperature of the surrounding mantle matter, and this must lead to a decrease of its pseudo-viscosity and its elastic limit. If the mantle current is still continuing, part of the down-buckled root must be carried along, and because of its smaller density it will remain at the mantle current's surface, and may be expected to be smeared out against the lower boundary of the crust in the foreland of the geosynclinal belt. Readjusting its isostatic equilibrium, this foreland crust must rise. We thus can explain why there has been a broad area of foreland rising in Europe, which forms the Mittelgebirge; the rivers flowing down from the geosynclinal mountain range, such as the Rhine and the Rhône, have cut valleys in this rising area. The morphology of these river valleys, as in the case of the Rhine valley between Mainz and Bonn, can only be understood by assuming a rise of this whole area. The rise has continued as far as the Ardennes and Limburg, and probably is still continuing. The fact that in these areas we find no strong folding, but only slight crustal deformation, accords well with this hypothesis about the origin of the Mittelgebirge. (See Fig.III.4).

In a large area of the Rocky Mountains, between the Front Range and the Coast Ranges, no marked folding is found. It is likely that we can explain its rise to a considerable elevation in the same way, that is, by the mantle currents transporting part of the down-buckled root of the Front Range in a westerly direction.

The above hypothesis concerning the origin of the Mittelgebirge also gives an explanation for another difficulty. The shortening of the crust in the Alpine area results from the folds and overthrusts of the crustal layers; a shortening of about 250 km has thus been calculated. Now the excess of crustal matter along this belt must in each cross-section amount to 250×35 km $= 8750$ km². If we put the cross-section of the present Alps at 150×2.5 km $= 375$ km² and of the isostatic root at 6.5 times as much, i.e., at 2438 km², there is a crustal excess of the cross-section of 2813 km². So we would have to assume that 5937 km² of the cross-section has disappeared by erosion, which is far too much. Here the hypothesis that the Mittelgebirge originated by the transportation of part of the down-buckled root of the Alps can explain where the crustal matter has gone. If we put the mean breadth of the Mittelgebirge at 600 km, their mean height at 0.6 km and their length at twice the length of the Alps, we have to increase the cross-section of the mountain ranges by 2×360 km² $= 720$ km². Together we thus obtain a figure of 1095 km² and for the combination of mountains and isostatic roots a figure of 7.5×1095 km $= 8212$ km². This result nearly equals the above figure of 8750 km² derived from the supposed crustal shortening. The small difference can easily be explained by the rough estimates made and by the effect of erosion. We may conclude that in this way we have found a strong argument in favour of our hypothesis about the origin of the Mittelgebirge. From this hypothesis it follows that the area of mountain formation caused by a geosynclinal belt can be very large; in the case of the Alpine belt it covers a great part of Europe.

The repeated precise levelling of The Netherlands has shown a rising of the southeastern part (Limburg) with regard to the northwestern coastal area. This might, perhaps, point to the continuation of the mantle current's effect of carrying the Alpine root matter northwestwards after a period of relaxation during which the Alpine ranges rose to a great elevation.

If this conclusion is true, it indicates that at least in the present geological period the mantle current may be interrupted by periods of relaxation. We might, perhaps, attribute this behaviour to the possibility that the mantle current, which may be supposed to have been going on since the beginning of the Tertiary, is close to accomplishing its half-turn. In that phase of the phenomenon we can accept that the dynamic equilibrium of the mantle is nearly readjusted, and that the current comes to a stop when the pressure gradient is no longer sufficient to overcome the elastic limit in the mantle. A small change in the heat distribution, e.g., by continued cooling at the surface, might then set it going again until it comes to a stop when the temperature gradients are again insufficient.

That in the present period we are in such conditions may perhaps explain why in the island-arc area southeast and east of Asia the currents appear to have continued – in Indonesia the Timor area seems the only one where the isostatic equilibrium was readjusted – while in the Alpine area a sufficient stress relaxation has occurred to allow the whole range to rise to great height.

Before leaving the subject of crustal down-buckling, it may be mentioned briefly that the melting of the down-buckled root and its subsequent consolidation may probably give a satisfactory explanation of the formation of granite. The high temperature and the high pressure to which the crustal root, which may contain sedimentary constituents, is subjected give the conditions appropriate for granitization, and this hypothesis agrees with the views expressed by READ (1955) that every mountain range is characterized by its own granite.

4. *Effects of horizontal tension in the crust*

In this Section we shall see that tension in the crust can lead to the formation of horsts and graben. According to the theory of faulting given by ANDERSON (1951), KING HUBBERT (1951), HAFNER (1951), and others, we may expect that horizontal

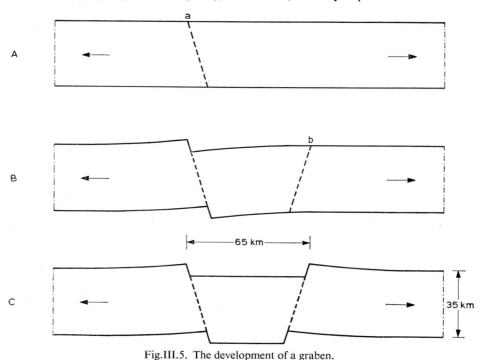

Fig.III.5. The development of a graben.

tension in the crust may lead to fault planes through the crust with an angle of hade of 25—30°.

In Fig.III.5A, one fault plane of this kind is indicated. The tendency to isostatic equilibrium must now bring about a further crustal deformation, at least if the two crustal parts can move apart sufficiently to allow relative movement along this fault plane. It must cause the left part to rise and the right part to subside, until for both parts isostatic equilibrium is readjusted. This stage is given by Fig.III.5B.

In many cases this phenomenon must lead to the development of a second fault plane. We can infer[1] that at a point b, the bending causes a maximum tensile stress of about 1200 kg/cm², and we may assume that the surface layer of the crust cannot stand this. It must lead to the formation of a second fault plane, which again must be expected to have an angle of hade of 25—30°. The tendency towards isostatic equilibrium must here also cause relative movements along that fault plane and, as shown by Fig.III.5C, this would lead to the formation of a graben and of two mountain ridges, one on each side of the graben. It can be deduced that the position of b, where the tension in the crust caused by the bending has a maximum value, is situated at a distance from the other side of the graben of about 65 km, and this figure is in good agreement with existing graben, e.g., the Upper Rhine graben between the Vosges and the Black Forest.

The formation of the second crustal fault plane in a direction converging downwards towards the first fault plane, and not in a direction parallel to it, is not easy to explain. The writer thinks it can be done by realizing that the horizontal dimension at the crust's surface can be shown to be proportional to the thickness T of the rigid crust to the power 3/4. Hence, if the crust is weakened by the creation at the surface of the second fault plane, we may suppose that lower down the distance of this plane from the first fault plane tends to be less. This might well lead to the second fault plane converging with regard to the first and, therefore, to the formation of a graben.

We have still to explain why the up-bending of the crustal parts to the left and to the right of the graben does not lead to the formation of a fault plane through the crust. Such a fault plane, however, has to start at the lower boundary of the crust, and it is easy to see that the great pressure as well as the greater plasticity at that depth prevent it from developing.

If over a wide area the crust is subject to tension, a second graben may form at some distance from the first, and this leads to the crustal block between the two diverging fault planes, which delimit the two graben, rising to form a "horst". The rise of the horst as well as the subsidence of the graben is a simple effect of adjustment of the isostatic equilibrium of the crustal blocks.

---

[1] For the derivation of this figure and for further details about the whole phenomenon, the reader may be referred to HEISKANEN and VENING MEINESZ, 1958, pp.390—394.

We find such a wide area of crustal tension throughout Europe between the Alpine arc and the North Sea and the Channel. It is no doubt caused by the diverging great mantle current system between the Alps and the coast, which carried along the Alpine root matter and thus is the origin of the French, Belgian, Dutch and German Mittelgebirge. Because of the diverging current directions there must be tension at right-angles to the current. In the southeast of The Netherlands, i.e., in South Limburg and the Peel area, it causes the well known horsts and graben in the surfaces of the Tertiary and deeper layers, which are so important for the exploitation of the coal deposits. This is only a small part of the horsts and graben present in the whole area.

It is interesting that in two areas of the Peel to the east of Eindhoven isostatic readjustment between horst and graben blocks is still going on. In 1930, it caused a light earthquake shock. At the surface, ridges in the sandy soil of a height of a few decimetres give evidence of these recent movements.

The most important belt of graben is found in the East African lake zone, reaching from Lake Nyasa to the Red Sea and continuing in the Dead Sea valley. The great crustal fault planes delimiting the belt of graben are accompanied by strong volcanicity, leading to several high volcanoes. Over this belt BULLARD (1936) carried out an important gravity survey. This gravity field is in harmony with the views given here. In his report Bullard derived theoretically the breadth of the graben, and arrived at the same result of 65 km, as given above. The writer cannot share his view that the belt is caused by horizontal compression in the crust.

5. *Belts of crustal wrench faulting usually accompanied by overriding*

We find such belts of crustal wrench faulting, accompanied by overriding, in the wing areas of island arcs, as in the Indonesian archipelago combined with the Philippine Islands, where it occurs in the Sumatra and Philippine parts of the tectonic belt. But we also find it in the high range of New Guinea, the Chilean part of the Andes, and probably likewise on the west coast of Mexico and of lower California.

We shall start by examining this phenomenon on the west coast of Sumatra. As we shall discuss in more detail in the next Section, we may assume that the crustal deformation in the whole Indonesian arc is caused by a mantle current in a direction given by an azimuth of about N165°E, slightly diverging in the eastern part to an azimuth of about N145°E. In the crust this current brings about a uniaxial compressional stress field in these directions. West of Sumatra the tectonic belt has a direction of N140°E. So here it encloses an angle of about 25° with the direction of the uniaxial stress. This value agrees with the angle that, according to the theory of faulting of ANDERSON (1951), KING HUBBERT (1951), HAFNER (1951), and others, must be expected between the stress and the fault plane.

Since, however, such a movement along a fault plane occurs on both sides of the

archipelago, and as these two fault planes converge in the direction of the movement of the Indonesian crustal block, these movements must be accompanied by
overriding on both sides of this block over the adjoining crustal blocks. There is
no evidence that the crustal compression in the direction at right-angles to the
movement of the whole Indonesian crustal block causes crustal deformation in the
block itself. This is probably due to the diverging mantle currents which localize
the compression in the border areas.

On the east side this overriding presses down the ocean floor to the east of the
Philippine Islands and leads to the formation of the Mindanao Trench. On the
west side it causes the rise in Sumatra of the Barisan range and the subsidence of
the Sumatra Trench to the west of that island. Both crustal zones are subject to
strong seismicity, obviously caused by the horizontal shear movements accompanied by overriding. In Fig.II.1 and 2, the gravity anomalies of the Indonesian
archipelago show that in these down-pressed belts anomalies of the order of —50
mgal occur, while in the down-buckled belts we find anomalies of more than —130
mgal. This checks with the crustal mass excesses in both areas, caused by the
horizontal compression of the crust; these crustal mass excesses are pressed down
in the mantle and thus displace heavier mantle matter.

The same mantle current, which east of the Philippine Islands presses down the
ocean floor, is probably responsible for the formation of the high mountain range of
West Irian. According to the research carried out by BÄR and VERSTAPPEN (1959)
during the West Irian expedition of 1961—62, this range is not due to folding and
overthrusting, but to wrench faulting combined with crustal overriding of the
northern block over the southern block along a huge fault plane. The azimuths of
the mantle current of about N140°E and that of the fault plane of about N110°E
are in good agreement with this supposition (VENING MEINESZ, 1961a).

We may probably assume that in the Chilean Andes similar wrench faulting combined with overriding occurs. In the next Chapter we shall find that below the
mid-ocean ridges we may expect rising mantle currents, and probably this is also
true for the Mid-Pacific Rise which runs from the South American coast near
Valdivia and Chiloé Island in an azimuth of about N60°W. So we may assume that
below the crust a mantle current is present which flows from there in an azimuth
of about N30°E. The drag exerted by this current on the crust may be expected to
be responsible for great wrench-faulting shear movements combined with overriding taking place along a huge fault plane in the axis of the Chilean Andes, which
runs in a direction of about N5°E. North of Chiloé Island this range is subject to
strong seismic activity, and this fits our supposition. We can probably assume that
this phenomenon is responsible for the formation of this part of the Andes. The
strong earthquake in Tolten in 1962 no doubt belongs to this seismic activity;
it gave a dextral relative displacement of over 6 m along the fault plane mentioned.

For our hypothesis regarding this part of the Andes we have to suppose that in an earlier period the South American continent was situated farther north, i.e., in such a position that the southernmost part of the Andes could also thus come into being. The southward shift of this continent that occurred since must be attributed to the whole system of currents present in the mantle.

The two gravity profiles at right-angles to the Chilean coast, observed by scientists of the Lamont Geological Observatory, are in good harmony with our hypothesis. For further details the reader may refer to VENING MEINESZ, 1964.

North of Arica, the west coast of South America and the Andes take a different trend, which is in an azimuth of about N25°W, and encloses an angle of 55° with the supposed underlying mantle current. So we may probably assume that here the principal crustal deformation has a down-buckling character, with strongly folded and overthrusted upper crustal layers. So far as the known geological data go, they support this view.

We shall now deal with another instance where it seems likely that wrench faulting combined with overriding has taken place. This is the southwest coast of San Salvador, Guatemala and Mexico. The data, however, are uncertain and incomplete. The supposition of a fault plane along this coast seems to be in harmony with the gravity profiles (VENING MEINESZ, 1948, pl. III, profiles 33, 34, 35 and 36) and with the evidence farther north, where in California the San Andreas Fault and other parallel fault planes occur. They show dextral shear movements and numerous earthquakes of a severe kind. This makes it probable that the shear movements are accompanied by overriding. This is also confirmed by the trenches along this coast. The gravity profiles have the same asymmetrical character as those observed on the west coast of Sumatra; this likewise points to overriding.

We may assume that the wrench faulting combined with overriding in this area is brought about by a convection current system under the North American continent. We shall discuss this current system further in Section V.2, where we shall find more confirmation of it; it must flow in a southerly direction.

In the next Section we shall deal with island arcs and we shall find evidence that crustal wrench faulting can also occur without being accompanied by overriding. It is likely that this is only possible if the fault plane is parallel to the mantle current to which the crustal deformation is due. In that case we have to assume that the velocity of the mantle current is quickly decreasing from below the crustal block on one side of the fault plane to below the crustal block on the other side, i.e., in a direction at right-angles to the fault plane.

This type of crustal wrench faulting is apparently not accompanied by earthquakes. This is probably owing to the absence of compressional stress normal to this plane, except what is present there because of the hydrostatic compression dependent on depth. The absence of earthquakes makes it difficult to find such fault planes. On a smaller scale such a phenomenon had already been noticed by GUTENBERG (1951, p.403), in the Buena Vista oil-field area in Kern County, California. He mentions the relative movements of two crustal blocks, shown by the bending of pipelines, for which during a number of years a relative velocity of 3 cm/year was observed. No shocks were felt. From the shearing off at various depths of the casing in wells, Gutenberg was able to determine the dip of the fault plane. It was approximately 25°.

6. *The crustal deformation in island-arc areas*

One of the greatest systems of crustal deformation is the island arc. In SECTION III. 2, we have already mentioned that the two central parts are formed by crustal down-buckling in belts, each enclosing an angle of 55° with the direction of the under-lying mantle current, which, therefore, bisects the angle of 110° between the two belts. The mantle current causes uniaxial compression in the crust, which brings about the crustal down-buckling. The tectonic belts on both wings of the arc are formed by crustal wrench faulting combined with overriding, as dealt with in the preceding Section. They enclose angles of 25—30° with the stress direction. The four parts of the tectonic belt may differ in length, and so usually the island arc is not symmetrical.

We shall now discuss two island-arc areas that have been sufficiently investigated for this purpose, the Indonesian and the Caribbean island arcs. The Indonesian arc, of which the gravity field is given by Fig.II.1 and 2, has a width of about 3000 km. The tectonic belt starts in Burmah, runs via the Andaman Islands, the Nicobar Islands, the islands west of Sumatra, the submarine ridge south of Java, over the Timor Trough and the southern edge of Timor, the Tanimbar Islands, the Kay Islands, to the Island of Buru. Another belt starts east of the Philippine Is-lands and runs over the Talaud Islands, the Celebes Sea and the eastern arm of Celebes. A weaker connection joins the Celebes Sea part to the end of the first belt in Buru. We may assume that the second belt stops where the eastern arm of Celebes joins the central part of that island.

The reason why in the eastern half of the archipelago the arc is broken and irregular is obviously the presence of the New Guinea buttress, where the crust is so much stronger that it resists plastic down-buckling.

The tectonic arc through the eastern arm of Celebes is no doubt subject to strong down-buckling; the isostatic anomalies in the Celebes Sea attain a maximum value of more than —200 mgal and the eastern arm shows evidence of strong folding and overthrusting. We may, therefore, assume that the corresponding crustal shorten-ing is large, probably of the order of 50—100 km. The crustal shortening, never-theless, stops at the western end of this arm, and thus we must assume a crustal fault plane, along which wrench faulting took place, running from this end in a northwestward direction, i.e., at right-angles to this arm. The fact that in the northern arm of Celebes, where this line cuts it, Ahlburg found geological evidence of faulting striking in this direction, appears to confirm this surmise (AHLBURG, 1913).

We thus should come to the supposition that there is a fault plane through the crust in a direction coinciding with that of the sub-crustal mantle current, along which horizontal shear took place. As, however, in the whole archipelago the seismic activity points to a continuation of the recent crustal deformation, and as this is also proved by the re-measuring, after an earthquake, of the triangulation in Tapanuli, mentioned in Section III.3, we may assume that in the Celebes area the crustal deformation likewise continues. However, in the supposed fault plane no earthquakes occur, and so it seems that here we have an example of the phenomenon mentioned at the end of the preceding Section.

In the Indonesian and Philippine archipelago we find several deep trenches. As we can readily understand, they occur in the wing areas as well as in the central area. In both types of areas the crust is pushed down and, if no sediment-providing land is near, this must lead to trench formation. There must, however, be two different types of trenches. If, as is the case for the Java Trench to the south of that island, the feature originates in the central area – in this case we shall speak of a "central trench" – it is caused by crustal down-buckling and, as we have discussed in Section III.3, it will disappear when the crustal compression vanishes. This occurs when the half-turn mantle current stops, i.e., at the end of the orogenic period.

In the case of the Java trench the island provides sediments, and so the trench is partly filled up and the remaining trench is shifted to the south with respect to the belt of negative anomalies. It might be possible, therefore, that by further sedimentation the trench will disappear before the end of the present orogenic period. At that time a mountain range will come into being.

If the trench occurs in the wing areas of the island arc, we shall call it a "wing trench". In the Indonesian—Philippine arc we find two wing trenches, the deep Mindanao Trench where a depth of 10,500 m has been recorded, and the Sumatra Trench to the west of the row of islands off the Sumatran west coast, where in the south a depth of 6200 m occurs.

In the case of the wing trenches the profile may be expected to be asymmetrical; the slope must be steeper on the land side than on the ocean side where it must taper off towards the ocean floor according to a bending curve of this floor. After the mantle current comes to a stop, the wing trenches cannot disappear by simple rising, as we may expect to be the general tendency for the central trenches.

In Section V.3, we shall make an attempt to classify the existing trenches according to whether they are central or wing trenches.

We have hitherto only examined the tectonic arc where the main crustal deformations occur. We shall now deal with the inner arc, which is marked by volcanoes. In the central part of the island arc this volcanic arc probably originates in the following way. The down-buckling of the crust here occurs in belts enclosing an angle of about 55° with the direction in which the whole archipel block is carried along by the mantle current. The crustal shortening associated with the down-buckling occurs, therefore, in a direction making an angle of about 35° with that of the archipel block-movement, and so the latter movement has a component parallel to the down-buckled belt which must also take place. It is obvious that the fault plane along which this shear movement occurs cannot be situated in the tectonic belt where crustal thickening and down-buckling increase the strength of the crust. For finding where this fault plane will originate we must realise that the greatest resistance to this shear movement must be located in the upper layer of the crust, which is colder and, therefore, more rigid than the lower part of the crust. Now the crustal down-buckling in the tectonic belt must, by the buoyancy of the down-pushed crustal root, cause an up-bending of a fairly broad crustal belt, spread over a much greater breadth than the down-buckled belt itself (see Fig.III.2), and we can prove that this up-bending causes a maximum of tension in the upper crustal layer at a distance of the order of 100—150 km. We may, therefore, expect that the fault plane or fault zone along which the relative movement parallel to the tectonic belt takes place, is situated at this same distance and on the inside of the arc. It is clear that this shear movement may be expected to lead to volcanic activity. We thus can explain why the tectonic arc is accompanied, at the distance mentioned, by a second arc or zone of volcanic character.

Inside the arc of this upward crustal wave the crustal deformation continues in a downward wave; in this third belt, however, the crust does not undergo plastic down-buckling. Such a crustal deformation would be unlikely as we should not be able to understand that in the same period the crust could give way by down-buckling in two parallel belts so near to each other. As, therefore, this downward wave is no real geosyncline, UMBGROVE (1932, 1933, 1934, 1947) proposed for it the name "idiogeosyncline" (see Fig.II.2). It carries oil, and so it is of great economic importance. The absence of a deep down-buckled root must render it improbable that an idiogeosyncline will ever lead to a high mountain range in the way a normal geosyncline does.

On the wings of the island arc the origin of the second volcanic arc probably has a similar cause to that in the central part. The overriding attending the crustal shear increases the strength of the crust and so we may expect that at a certain time a new fault plane, more landwards, will come into action. On both wings of the arc these fault planes will be the continuation of the inner arc in the central part of the island arc. Because of the difference in direction at these joining points we may expect increased seismic activity there, as is the case in Sunda Strait between Sumatra and Java. In this connection it may be pointed out that in these joining areas between wing and central parts, the tectonic arc may be expected to show a curved transition between the belts of crustal deformation.

In several island arcs, as, for example, the Caribbean arc, the crustal compression is not yet sufficiently released to allow the tectonic arc to rise above sea-level

– in the Caribbean arc this is only the case for the islands of Barbados, Tobago and Trinidad – and the result is that only the inner, volcanic, arc is visible above sea-level.

The fact that in the present period the volcanoes of the volcanic island arcs are throwing out more acid matter than other volcanic islands, which are not situated in an island arc area, e.g., Madeira and Hawaii, is probably due to the sialic character of the down-buckled roots of the tectonic arcs that owing to the high temperature become more plastic and are mixing with the sub-crustal mantle matter thrown out in the volcanic arcs. We shall come back to this point in Section IV.9.

In order to explain the crustal deformations in the Indonesian archipelago we have to assume a mantle current system of great dimensions, rising under Asia and flowing out under the archipelago in directions slowly changing from an azimuth of N165°E in the western part to N145°E in the eastern part, and to N140°E in the Philippine Islands area. The enormous size of the current system indicates a mantle current revolving over the full thickness of the mantle. In Chapter V, we shall see that, according to the island arcs present, this current system continues over the whole east coast of Asia, and that over a great distance it keeps the last mentioned direction in an azimuth of about N140°E. In Chapter IV, this will provide us with one of the strongest arguments in favour of the hypothesis of mantle currents.

We shall now briefly examine the Caribbean Islands arc, which we have already mentioned. Examining the tectonic arc as it is shown by the belt of strong negative anomalies, we find that the belt starts north of Cape Maisi (southeast Cuba), runs over the Puerto Rico Trench, follows a track outside the Antillean volcanic arc and runs over Barbados, Tobago, Trinidad and the adjoining part of Venezuela; from Barbados to Trinidad the negative anomalies are smaller. In Venezuela the anomaly belt is offset to the north-northeast for about 250 km; it continues west-ward, just north of the islands of Bonaire, Curaçao and Aruba, and north of the Goajira Peninsula. The belt suddenly ends north of the mouth of the Magdalena River.

It appears legitimate again to suppose that the belts of strong negative anomalies are caused by the down-buckling of the crust. This would lead to the hypothesis that a mantle current flows in an azimuth of N35°E from below the South American continent. This would classify the Puerto Rico Trench, of which the axis has a west—east direction, as a central trench. The central part would then run from north of Cape Maisi up to Barbados, and from Trinidad to Venezuela, while the whole offset belt from north-northeast of the end of the former belt to the end of this belt north of the mouth of the Magdalena River, also belongs to the central parts. From Barbados over Tobago to Trinidad the belt must be of the wing type. This is in harmony with the much smaller values there of the negative anomalies.

In this area are two fault planes parallel to the supposed mantle current, along which horizontal wrench-faulting movements take place. Firstly, we find one in the offset north of Venezuela, where the horizontal shortening of the crust in the down-buckling belts cannot take place without such wrench faulting; and secondly, such wrench faulting must occur along a fault plane connecting the end of the down-buckled belt north of Cape Maisi with the end of the down-buckled belt north of the Magdalena River. This fault plane also has the direction of the supposed mantle current.

Probably this last fault plane continues up to the twisted part of the Isthmus, which is in line with it. If this supposition is right, we may probably assume that in the course of the earth's history this curious twist came into being by a relative movement of about 200 km of the South American continent with respect to Central and North America.

Both shear movements mentioned are, at least in the present period, not accompanied by earthquakes. This checks with our views about this type of shear.

In the above discussion of the crustal deformations in island-arc areas, no mention was made of the subsidence of the deep basins in these areas, e.g., the Banda Sea and the Caribbean Sea, or of the third arcs which are probably connected with these phenomena. For these subjects the reader may refer to Section IV.9.

7. *Crustal phenomena and deformations in the ocean crust*

It is likely that plastic down-buckling of the crust, effects of horizontal tension in the crust, and crustal wrench faulting, also occur in the ocean crust. We shall see that the first phenomenon has great geophysical importance.

Outside the sedimentation belt surrounding the continents the oceanic crust probably consists of only a thin layer of basalt a few kilometres thick, possibly covered by a few kilometres of sediments. Below that the bulk of the crust consists mainly of the same olivine which forms the upper mantle, but at a lower temperature than at greater depth and, therefore, having a higher elastic limit and higher viscosity. So the temperature dominates the physical behaviour of the ocean crust.

In the above statement we have, however, not mentioned that turbidity currents (see Kuenen's papers and books about this subject: KUENEN and HUMBERT, 1964) bring sediments to great distances from the continental coasts. Large areas in the oceans will thus no doubt have a sedimentary layer, consolidated as well as unconsolidated, of considerable thickness. We shall, however, restrict ourselves here to those parts of the oceans where the above crustal constitution exists. A study of the other areas will be reserved for another occasion.

If the ocean crust is subject to uniaxial horizontal compression exceeding the elastic limit, it will deform plastically in the same way as we described for the continental crust in Section III.2; a similar plastic down-buckling must occur. Obviously in this process the extreme smallness of the heat conduction again plays the

51

decisive part. The downbuckled crustal root must retain its lower temperature with regard to the surrounding mantle matter for a relatively long period. The fact, however, that for a great part the down-buckling root consists of the same olivine, and that consequently the root has nearly the same density as the mantle, must facilitate the pushing down of the root compared with the same process in the continents. We can, therefore, understand why the root would be pushed down to a considerably greater depth. As the root gradually assumes the higher temperature of the adjoining mantle, it must even tend to be swallowed up by the mantle.

So we may assume that in the oceans the plastic down-buckling process leads to a much greater shortening of the crust than in the continents. If we neglect the small content of basalt and sediments, we might even suppose that the crustal shortening in these oceanic geosynclines is unlimited.

We thus arrive at a conclusion of immense importance in the geophysical history of the earth, i.e., the possibility that the mantle currents can transport the continents over the earth's surface without their undergoing much deformation. We likewise see that this conclusion is right, notwithstanding the rigid character of the earth's crust below the oceans, which is shown by many straight fault planes through this crust, of which evidence is given by the Menard escarpments and by a considerable number of straight rows of volcanic islands and atolls in the Western and Middle Pacific. Because of the numerous arguments in favour of continental drift, given by TAYLOR (1910), WEGENER (1929) and more recently by RUNCORN (1963), this is a welcome conclusion. To the older arguments, Runcorn added important and strong arguments based on the magnetization of rocks, which has such a stability that a disagreement of their magnetic properties with regard to the magnetic field now present at the places where these rocks are located, provides us with a strong indication of the mobility of the earth's surface. In Section IV.10, we shall come back to this important subject of continental drift.

The Menard escarpments in the Pacific Ocean floor to the west of North and Central America are probably caused by wrench faulting along fault planes through the ocean crust, combined with overriding. So this is the same crustal process that was dealt with in Section III.5 for the continents. As we shall discuss in the next Chapter, the mid-ocean ridges may be expected to overlie rising mantle currents, and according to Menard's map of these ridges (Fig.III.6) the Mid-Pacific Rise between Japan and the Bonin Islands on one side and South America on the other side has in the area concerned an azimuth of about N35°W. The mantle current between that rise and the west coast of California and Mexico may, therefore, be expected to have an azimuth of about N55°E. This direction encloses an angle of about 25—30° with Menard's escarpments, which have an azimuth of N80°E—N85°E, and so this agrees with our hypothesis of a wrench-faulting origin

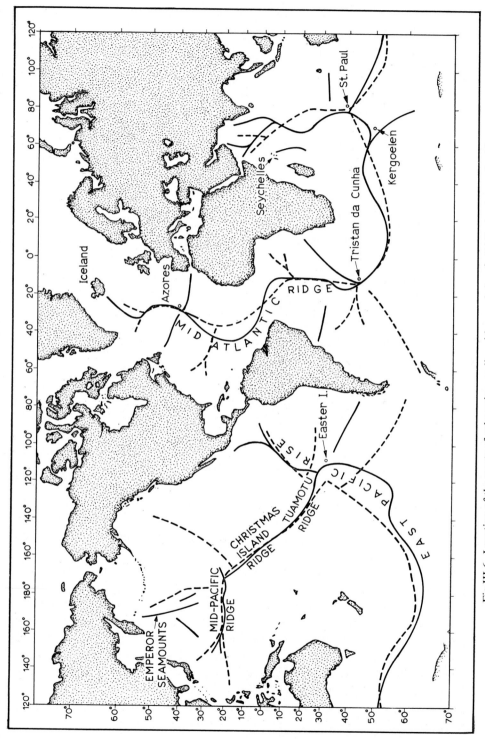

Fig.III.6. Location of the crests of submarine median ridges and rises (solid line) compared with the geometrical median line (dashed) of the ocean basins. (After MENARD, 1959).

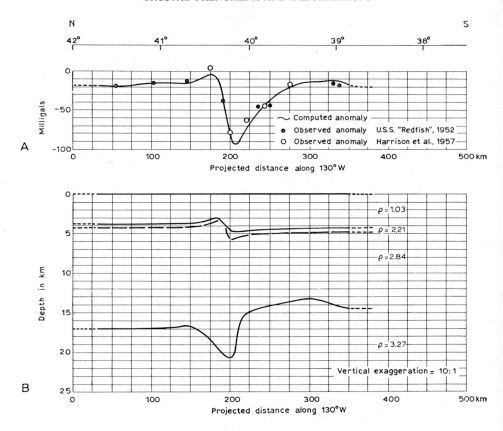

Fig.III.7. Free-air anomalies (A) and the deduced crustal structure (B) under the Mendocino fracture zone (with assumed sedimentary layer). (After TALWANI et al., 1959).

of these escarpments. Menard's topographical and gravimetric profiles over one of these features (Fig.III.7) clearly show that it probably originated by wrench fault-ing, combined with overriding of the northern crustal block over the southern one.

   The diminishing of the mantle current velocity from southeast towards northwest, which can explain why the crust in this area was subject to wrench faulting com-bined with overriding, can probably be accounted for by the mantle current in the northwest area being slowed down by the presence of the North American conti-nent, under which we may suppose that there is a rising mantle current flowing off below the crust in a southerly direction. In Central America no such mantle current is preventing the flow of the current here dealt with. Its presence there is even likely because we can probably attribute to it the formation of the Cayman Trough zone with the Bartlett and Oriente Deeps. Its effect, however, does not appear to reach to the crustal block to the southeast of the aseismic fault plane from Panama to Cape Maisi, dealt with in the preceding Section.

54

We may conclude that the two crustal phenomena of down-buckling, which for the continental areas have been discussed in Section III.2, and of shear combined with overriding, which for the continents has been dealt with in Section III.5, are also found in the oceanic crust. It can, however, easily be seen that in the oceanic crust the effect of horizontal tension differs considerably from that in the continental crust, which has been discussed in Section III.4. Because of the small density difference between the rigid ocean crust and the underlying mantle, it is not likely that a fault plane, caused by horizontal tension and having an angle of hade of 25—30°, leads to enough down-bending of the crust on one side of the fault plane to cause the formation of a second fault plane as occurs in the continental crust. As a consequence of this it does not seem probable that a graben will be formed in the same way as in the continent.

One effect of the fault plane caused by tension in the crust remains important in the oceans also. This is the appearance of volcanoes along that plane. A row of volcanic islands, guyots, and submarine volcanoes can reveal a crustal fault plane, and obviously this may be caused by horizontal tension in the crust.

As we shall see in Section V.1, we must suppose that below the mid-ocean ridges we generally find rising limbs of mantle currents and, as a consequence of this, we may expect horizontal tension in the crust. It is in harmony with this supposition that on these mid-ocean rises we often find volcanic islands and submarine volcanoes. Of the latter the writer found much evidence in sounding profiles over the Mid-Atlantic Rise. By soundings and gravity determinations he was able to prove that the Romanche Deep, which is found on the Mid-Atlantic Rise just south of the equator, is no trench; it probably is a caldeira, and so it is likely also to have a volcanic origin (VENING MEINESZ, 1948, p.118, pl. III, profiles 38 and 38a).

Scientists of the Lamont Geological Observatory found evidence in the mid-ocean rises of lighter materials, and this may, perhaps, lead to the possibility of graben formation. On top of these rises they found over large distances a graben or rift. This feature appears to confirm the supposition of horizontal tension in the crust, and this is in agreement with the hypothesis of rising mantle currents below the mid-ocean ridges, whether this feature is a graben of the same type as the graben on the continents or a rift of another type.

Chapter IV

CONVECTION CURRENTS IN THE MANTLE

1. *Arguments in favour of mantle convection currents*

There are many arguments pointing to the presence of currents in the mantle; it is obvious that probably these currents have the character of convection currents caused by the cooling at the earth's surface. This cooling, brought about by radiation and by heat conduction, does not imply that the earth as a whole is cooling. Radioactive constituents may easily produce as much or even more heat than is lost at the surface.

One argument in favour of mantle currents and against the contraction theory is the presence at the same time in some areas of crustal down-buckling caused by horizontal compression, and in other areas of graben formation indicating horizontal tension. It is difficult to account for this otherwise than by assuming mantle currents exerting drag forces on the crust in different directions. The same is true if we want to explain the great relative displacements of crustal blocks along fault planes, as in the case of the San Andreas Fault and parallel faults in California, where the displacement occurs shockwise and is accompanied by strong earthquakes, but where it always continues in the same sense, and in total amounts to many hundreds of kilometres. Many other instances of such large relative displacements can be given, such as along the Great Glen Fault in Scotland.

A further argument in favour of the mantle current hypothesis may be derived from the evidence, obtained in island-arc areas, about extensive fields of uniaxial compression in the crust. This, likewise, is hard to account for without admitting mantle currents of great size exerting a drag on the crust in the given direction.

As has already been briefly set out in Chapter I, p. 4, and as we shall discuss in more detail in Section IV.7, the mantle currents only make a half-turn, bringing down the cooled upper layer which by cooling became denser, and bringing up the lower layer of high temperature matter which therefore has a lower density. We may suppose that this half-turn current lasts about 50—100 million years, during which time the crust is subject to orogeny. When the half-turn is completed, dynamic equilibrium is regained and the movement stops. The thermal conditions, however, are strongly disturbed; the upper layer has a relatively high temperature and the lower layer a relatively low one. This period must, therefore, be characterized by a high temperature gradient at the top as well as at the base of the mantle, and the consequence must be a relatively strong thermal flow and radiation at the surface, and also thermal flow from the core to the lower mantle layer. This period of rest in the mantle must last until the original conditions are restored, namely, a cooled upper mantle layer and a hot lower layer. The situation is then mature for a new half-turn mantle current, and consequently for a new period of orogeny at the crust's surface. From the interval between successive periods of orogeny we can estimate that these periods of rest in the mantle last some 200—300 million years. The possibility of thus explaining the intermittent occurrence of orogenic periods provides us with a new argument in favour of mantle convection currents.

A further argument may be derived from the way in which a geosyncline, originating during an orogenic period, can not only lead to the forming of a folded mountain range but also of Mittelgebirge. As has been set forth in Section III.3, the down-buckled root of a geosyncline gradually becomes plastic and can be transported by the underlying mantle current along the lower boundary of the crust towards the foreland; the crustal matter is thus added to the foreland crust and lifts it up, thus forming the Mittelgebirge. So this way of explaining the origin of the Mittelgebirge also requires the presence of mantle currents.

A third argument connected with the above explanation of orogeny in geosynclines, is provided by the way we can explain the regressions usually accompanying orogeny during the early stages, and the transgressions prevailing in a later stage. Because of the greater amounts of radioactive matter in the crust of the continents as compared with that of the oceans, we may suppose a higher mantle temperature to exist below the continents and, therefore, that rising currents will occur there and especially under the continental borders. When the half-turn currents have accomplished a quarter turn, there must be a maximum temperature difference between the rising limbs of the currents and the subsiding limbs, and so, because of the thermal expansion effect, we may then expect a maximum rising of the continental borders and a maximum subsidence of the adjoining ocean areas. This, therefore, means a period of maximum regression. During the second quarter-turn of the mantle flow this regression must gradually disappear and must change to a transgression. This period of transgression may be expected to last during the whole period of rest.

It has already been mentioned that the time of maximum regression marks a period of maximum difference of mean temperature between the rising and subsiding current columns, and so it follows that it also is a time of maximum driving power of the convection currents.

Another argument in favour of mantle currents is provided by BOWEN's (1928) theory about the formation of basalt. He assumes that presssure relief brings about selective fusion of peridotite, whereby basaltic magma and olivine are formed, the latter remaining in the solid state. However, this process must soon have caused the upper mantle to lose its basalt and become barren. The problem thus arises of how we can account for the continuation throughout the earth's entire history of the forming of basalt. Evidently we can solve this problem by assuming episodically recurring mantle currents, which bring new peridotite to the surface, producing new basaltic magma. It is even possible that the slight increase of density attending the change of peridotite into olivine contributes to the driving power of the mantle currents.

Furthermore, we may refer to Section IV.4, in which we shall deal with a spherical harmonic development of the topographical elevations at the earth's surface. We shall find that the distribution of the topography shows a clear correlation with the distribution over the mantle of convection current systems. Obviously this is a strong indication that such currents have played a large part with regard to the origin of the surface relief and, therefore, with regard to the deformations of the earth's crust. At the same time this provides a further proof of the existence of mantle currents.

A last group of arguments in favour of mantle currents is provided by the many indications of movements of continents relative to the poles and to each other. These arguments have partly a geomagnetic character (RUNCORN, 1963) and partly a different origin (WEGENER, 1929, and others). In Section IV.10, we shall briefly deal with these arguments.

Taking all these arguments together the writer thinks that the presence of mantle currents may be considered as practically certain.

2. *The transition layer between 500 and 900 km depth in connection with mantle currents*

From seismic research it has been deduced that between a depth of 500 and 900 km the density increases much more than corresponds to the increasing pressure. The density excess amounts to about 0.6 g/cm³. It can, however, not be doubted that the mantle convection currents move through this layer. If, for example, we consider the great area of the Indonesian archipelago, which must be affected over its whole extent by mantle current drag in nearly the same direction, we must conclude that the mantle current revolves over the full height of the mantle. It would be quite impossible for the current to make its revolution in the upper 500 km of the mantle.

This conclusion renders it probable, if not certain, that the olivine, of which the upper mantle layer mainly consists, has another modification of a density about 0.6 g/cm³ larger, which it assumes under great pressure. This supposition was put forward by BERNAL (1936) who suggested that the second phase probably has a cubic character; the olivine of the mantle would change to spinel under high pressure.

In taking up this matter the writer was fortunate to get the collaboration of Dr. E.J.W. Verwey, Director of the Philips Laboratories in Eindhoven (The Netherlands), and of two scientists of these laboratories, who wrote an important paper about it (MEIJERING and ROOYMANS, 1958). Their conclusions are summarized in the following:

A treatment of the mantle transition layer as a transition of a one-component system, $(Mg, Fe)_2SiO_4$, from the orthorhombic to the spinel form does not yield satisfactory results. Clapeyron's law, given by:

$$\frac{dT}{dP} = \frac{dV}{dS}$$

in which T is the absolute temperature, P the pressure, V the volume and S the entropy, provides a downward temperature gradient of $3.6°/km$ over the whole transition layer, and this is more than can be present; besides other considerations, the fact that the density discontinuity in the core at a depth of about 5100 km is probably caused by a change of the iron to a solid state, fixes the temperature at that depth at about 4000°, which is incompatible with the above temperature gradient.

A treatment of the matter in the transition layer as a binary system, Mg_2SiO_4—Fe_2SiO_4, gives us better results, but this, too, is not satisfactory, since it makes it probable that in this case the phase transition would split up into two fairly thin layers near the upper and lower boundaries of the transition layer, and this does not agree with the seismic data about this layer.

The authors come to the conclusion that the matter in the transition layer must be at least a ternary system, probably Mg_2SiO_4, Fe_2SiO_4, $MgSiO_3$, but that it is likely that still more constituents are present, e.g., Na, K, Ca, Al, etc. The constitution of the mantle would then comprise the following four layers, of which the two middle ones would together form the density transition layer:

1. Olivine + enstatite, in which the crystal lattice would not dissolve the above named other constituents (Na, K, Ca, Al, etc.). It would, therefore, be a heterogeneous layer, and its physical properties would be an average of those of its constituents.
2. Spinel + olivine + enstatite ⎱ transition layer;
3. Spinel + enstatite ⎰ the density curve may show one or more kinks.
4. Spinel in the whole layer of the mantle below the transition layer.

The spinel lattice is tolerant and so Na, K, Ca, Al, etc., can occupy cation vacancies in this lattice.

It is clear that this state of things must lead to reactions if the pressure changes while the temperature remains the same. On loading of the crust, part of the olivine will change into the denser crystal form, i.e., into spinel, and this must be accomplished by the release of a transition heat which we shall denote as K cal/g. Evidently this transition must obey Clapeyron's law which says:

$$\frac{dP}{dT} = \frac{KA}{T \Delta V}$$

where P is the pressure, T the absolute temperature, ΔV the change in volume and

A the heat equivalent equalling $4.19 \cdot 10^7$ cal./g cm² t². We shall not attempt a solution of these thermodynamic problems here, but we may restrict ourselves to the remark that an unloading of the crust, e.g., by the disappearance of an ice load, must be accompanied by three phenomena at the crust's surface, i.e., a rapid elastic rebound, a somewhat slower rise because of the reaction of the transition layer (change of spinel into olivine) and a still slower rise caused by the tendency towards isostatic readjustment (see also Section II.2). The latter movement is brought about by pseudo-flow in the mantle resulting from the differences of pressure in the mantle caused by the disappearing of the ice load. The rising curve for Fennoscandia, derived from old shorelines, varves, marigraphs and tide gauges, repeated levellings, etc., is in good agreement with the hypothesis of these three causes of rising. Since the disappearance of the ice some 10,000 years ago, the isostatic readjustment has proceeded to about two-thirds of the original deviation from isostatic equilibrium; the elastic rebound must have been nearly instantaneous, and the process of reaction in the transition layer seems to have taken place in about 2000—3000 years.

In this fairly simple case of flow in the mantle the observed facts allow a surmise about the part played by the transition layer. For convection currents in the mantle the problem is more complicated. The authors mentioned above, in their paper on the thermodynamic problems of the mantle and of the transition layer, state their opinion that convection currents can break through this layer and that its presence even favours these currents. In a study (HEISKANEN and VENING MEINESZ, 1958, pp. 406, 407) the writer came to the conclusion that probably this layer causes the driving power of the mantle convection currents to be more than four times greater than would be the case if the mantle were homogeneous and if the convection current, therefore, could derive its driving power only from the downward temperature gradient.

In this connection the possibility may be mentioned that without the instability caused by the transition layer the driving power, caused by the temperature gradient, would be insufficient to overcome the strength of the crystalline mantle. This raises the thought that the earth's cooling may lead to a gradual increase of the spinel and a corresponding decrease of the olivine, and that, if this continues, the time might come when no olivine would be left and in this way the possibility of mantle convection currents would vanish. For the earth this speculation no doubt only has a bearing on the distant future. There is, however, the possibility that in the present period it may already apply to another planet or to other celestial bodies.

3. *Spherical harmonic development of the earth's topography*

In 1922, PREY published a spherical harmonic development up to the 16th order of the earth's topography; it had taken him three years to carry out the calculations. Because of the great increase of knowledge since obtained about the topography in the water-covered areas, which account for about 71% of the earth's surface, and also because of the important conclusions the writer arrived at by studying Prey's results and the wish to extend the development to higher orders, a new development was made in 1957 in The Netherlands. It was taken to the 31st order. The work was made possible by a grant from the Netherlands Foundation for Pure Scientific Research in The Hague. The 40,680 data about the earth's topography, required for this development, were provided by the Netherlands Geodetic Commission and especially by its member Prof. Ir. G.J. Bruins and his assistants. The main purpose of this study is to determine the periodicities in the distribution over the earth's surface of the topographic features.

Before going into details about the results, the writer will attempt to explain the meaning of such a development without going into complicated mathematical details. For this purpose we start with a quantity q having different values along a circle; as an example we may take the topographic elevation along the equator. If we want to express this quantity as a function of the angle λ between a radius of the circle to a certain point on it chosen as zero point, and the radius of the point we want to define – for the equator we should call it the geographical longitude of this point –, we can use the Fourier development, which up to the order n is given by:

$$q = q_m + A_1 \cos\lambda + A_2 \cos 2\lambda + \ldots + A_p \cos p\lambda + \ldots A_n \cos n\lambda$$
$$+ B_1 \sin\lambda + B_2 \sin 2\lambda + \ldots + B_p \sin p\lambda + \ldots B_n \sin n\lambda \tag{1}$$

in which q_m is the mean value of q over the whole circle and A_1, B_1, A_2, B_2, ... A_p, B_p, ... A_n, B_n coefficients in such a way adapted to the quantity q that the sum of the series of terms represents q as closely as is possible.

We see that this formula obeys the condition that, if λ has a value larger than $360°$ the terms repeat their values and that, therefore, the formula remains valid. We also see that if we extend the series up to a higher order n, the formula represents q in more detail.

For a function on a sphere, such as the topographic elevation over the earth (for our purposes we can neglect the flattening and consider the earth as spherical), we can follow the same line, but as each point is given by two coordinates, for which we shall choose the longitude λ and the distance ϑ to the pole which, therefore, is the complement of the latitude, the formula becomes more complicated. We call this the spherical harmonic development of our quantity.

For the spherical harmonic development formula (1) is still valid, but the coefficients A and B are now functions of ϑ. Writing it in the usual way, we find for the nth order term of our quantity q:

$$q_n = a_n P_n + a_{n_1} P_n^1 \cos\lambda + \ldots + a_{np} P_n^p \cos p\lambda + \ldots + a_{nn} P_n^n \cos n\lambda$$
$$+ b_{n_1} P_n^1 \sin\lambda + \ldots + b_{np} P_n^p \sin p\lambda + \ldots + b_{nn} P_n^n \sin n\lambda \tag{2}$$

in which the coefficients a and b are adapted to the quantity q, and the quantities P represent functions of ϑ only. We give the relevant formulae in the appendix to this Chapter. From these formulae and from formula (2) it follows that the first term of (2), which is called the "Legendre" or "zonal" term, is constant along the parallels; it is zero on n parallels which separate positive and negative zones. The last terms of (2), which are called the "sectorial" terms, are periodic along the equator and the parallels, and change on each meridian from a maximum at the equator to zero at the two poles. The terms indicated in (2) by the sub-order p show p meridians and $n—p$ parallels where they are zero and the areas between are alternatingly positive and negative. These terms are called the "tesseral" terms [1].

Each quantity on the sphere can be represented by such a series of spherical harmonic terms and the representation is more true in detail the higher the order n to which the development has been carried out. As we see in (2) the number of sub-terms for the nth order is $2n + 1$. It readily follows that this leads to a total number of $(n + 1)^2$ terms for the series up to the order n. So the development of the topographic elevation mentioned comprises 1024 terms up to the 31st order. Still this development is not fine enough for representing topographic features of less than about 500—1000 km in diameter.

Neither for Prey's development comprising 289 terms, nor for the recent one of 1024 terms, could any system or regularity in these terms be discovered. However, in 1951, the writer obtained a remarkable result in the following way. In taking up a study of a possible correlation between the topography and mantle currents, he found that the Rayleigh number of mantle currents, which dominates their probability, depends only on the order of the spherical harmonics according to which such currents are distributed and not on the subterms of that order. This led him to derive for each order n a representative figure of the $2n + 1$ sub-terms of the spherical harmonic development of the topography. For this representative figure he chose the root mean square of the elevations corresponding to the $2n + 1$ sub-terms of that order in the spherical harmonic development of the topography mentioned above. The mean square of the elevations of order n is given by the formula:

---

[1] In order to give an idea of the low order terms of a spherical harmonic development it may be mentioned that a first order term may be represented as the distance between the sphere and a second sphere of the same size which is shifted over a small distance with regard to the first. The shift can be defined by its three orthogonal components with regard to a given orthogonal coordinate system; this checks with the number of $2n + 1$ coefficients for the nth order term.

The second order term can be represented by the distance from the sphere to a co-centric triaxial ellipsoid of the same volume which does not deviate much from the sphere. It is easy to see that this ellipsoid requires five coefficients to define it in shape and position.

The distances mentioned in this short note are supposed to be small enough that the square of the distance divided by the radius of the sphere is negligible.

$$\left|(q_n)^2\right| = \frac{1}{2n+1}\, a_n^2 + \frac{(n+1)!}{2(2n+1)(n-1)!}\,(a_{n1}^2 + b_{n1}^2) + \dots$$

$$+ \frac{(n+p)!}{2(2n+1)(n-p)!}\,(a_{np}^2 + b_{np}^2) + \dots + \frac{2n!}{2(2n+1)}\,(a_{nn}^2 + b_{nn}^2) \qquad (3)$$

In view of its physical meaning the right-hand member of this formula must be invariant with regard to changes of coordinates of the spherical harmonic system.

In Fig.IV.1, the ordinates represent the root mean square of the elevations of order n for all the orders from 1—31, and we see how remarkably regular this curve is. This regularity shows that there must be a physical cause behind it. In the next Section, we shall find that probably this is provided by convection currents in the mantle. It is interesting to realize that this regularity can only be discovered by the development of the topographic elevations in spherical harmonics.

In order to facilitate the study in the next Section of the correlation of the topography with mantle currents, Fig.IV.1 also shows a hatched curve representing the inverse values of the Rayleigh numbers for mantle currents distributed according to the corresponding spherical harmonics. Obviously there was no reason to continue this curve for higher orders than the seventh. The inverse values represented by the curve give a measure for the probabilities of mantle currents being distributed according to the corresponding spherical harmonics.

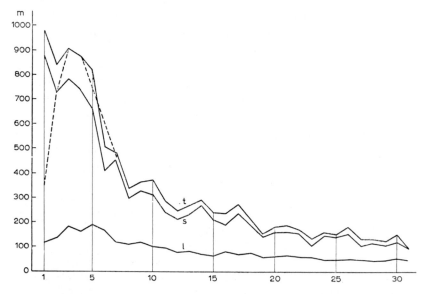

Fig.IV.1. Spherical harmonic development of the earth's topography; representative figures; t = total topography; s = ocean floor topography; l = continental topography.

Besides the main curve, Fig.IV.1 also gives a second curve of which the ordinates represent a second spherical harmonic development which takes account of the ocean topography only; for this development the topography in the continents was put at zero. Such a second development was also carried out by Prey.

From the complete spherical harmonic development combined with the second development it was easy to derive a third one having regard to the continents only, putting the oceanic elevations at zero. For this purpose the differences were taken of the 1024 coefficients of the total development and the 1024 coefficients of the second development for the oceans only. The 1024 differences form a third set of coefficients which take note of the continents only. Also for this set the root mean square of the elevations for each order was derived. The results are given by the third curve of Fig.IV.1.

4. *Interpretation of the spherical harmonic developments, history of the earth*

The curves in Fig.IV.1 of the total development and the oceanic development show much larger ordinates than that for the continental development. It is clear that this is brought about by the fact that by far the most important topography of the earth with regard to sea level is given by the presence of the deep oceanic basins which cover together about 71% of the total surface. In comparison with this topography the continental topography is much smaller.

In the curves of the total development and the oceanic development a strong peak is seen for the first order term. Obviously this is the expression of the well-known fact that one hemisphere has more of the continental areas than the other hemisphere. The difference is largest if we choose the first hemisphere around a point east of Constanza and south of Odessa.

This point is in fact given by the axis of the first order term of the spherical harmonic development.

Although still large, the ordinate for the second order is decidedly smaller. Then we get a prominent wave of the orders 3, 4 and 5, but after that the ordinates decrease and this in general seems to continue, but with waves and irregularities, for further increasing values of n. Before discussing the details mentioned we shall first look at this general tendency.

We can probably explain it by realizing that the order n is inversely proportional to the horizontal dimensions of the topography of that order, and as the vertical dimensions of the topography have a tendency to be proportional to the horizontal dimensions, we come to the conclusion that in general the vertical ordinates may be expected to diminish for the higher values of n. By this reasoning we also understand that this is no longer valid for low values for n for which the horizontal dimensions of the topography are so large that the proportionality to the elevation is no longer true.

65

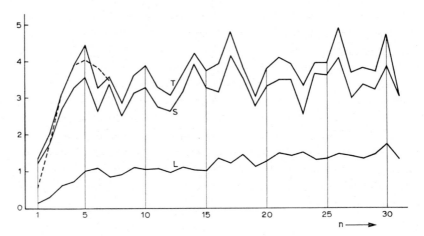

Fig.IV.2. Ordinates of Fig.IV.1, multiplied by $n^{\frac{1}{2}}(n + 1)^{\frac{1}{2}}$, giving T, S, and L.

In order to study the smaller features better for higher values of n we have multiplied all curves by $n^{\frac{1}{2}}(n + 1)^{\frac{1}{2}}$, which for reasons given in HEISKANEN and VENING MEINESZ (1958, pp.428, 429), has some advantage over a multiplication by n. The resulting curves are given in Fig.IV.2. Indeed, for $n > 5$ they have a general tendency to be horizontal. For our studies we shall use both figures.

They reveal three main phases of the earth's history, which are disclosed by the spherical harmonic development of the earth's topography. During the oldest phase the core and an ur-continent were formed; during the next phase the mantle still had more or less the character of a Newtonian fluid, although probably of high viscosity, and during this phase the currents in the mantle tore apart the ur-continent and pushed together shields in the crust; lastly, during the third phase, which still is going on, the mantle has crystallized and is only intermittently subject to systems of convection currents which have mainly a sectorial nature and cause deformations in the crust with a geosyncline or a graben and horst character.

The first phase of the earth's history probably started with an undifferentiated earth at a high temperature. How this phase came into being falls outside the scope of this book. The cooling at the surface, chiefly by radiation, must have caused instability leading to convection currents. Because the earth in this earliest phase probably had the properties of a viscous Newtonian fluid, the writer could apply the hydrodynamical laws in his studies, and found the current pattern given by Fig.IV. 3. For these deductions reference may be made to HEISKANEN and VENING MEINESZ, 1958, especially pp. 421—432. In these pages he made it clear that for the convection the first order current distribution, as given by Fig.IV.3, was by far the most likely to arise. This is an interesting result, because it might be thought that such a one-directional solution could not come into being without outside

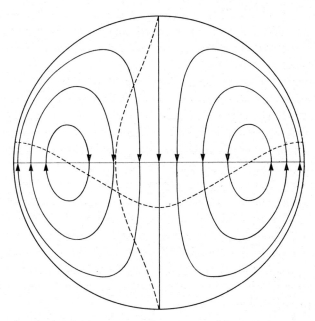

Fig.IV.3. First-order current in a fluid undifferentiated earth during an early stage of its history; dashed curves give the velocity distribution in axis and equator of the current system.

influences. This, however, does not appear to be necessary, although of course it might be possible that the attraction of the moon, which in this early period of the earth's history must have been considerably nearer to the earth than now, had an effect.

It is clear that this first order current must have led to a differentiation and that the heavy metals were concentrated by the current into a gradually growing core, whereas the light sialic constituents were left at the surface. The latter must have been pushed together by the current into an ur-continent located above the descending limb of the current. It appears probable that at that time it was compressed to an area of about 29% of the earth's surface, which is still the total area of the continental matter. It might have been slightly different, but a large change does not seem likely.

The growing core must after some time have stopped the first order current; this current distribution no longer represented the least-resistance solution. The currents, in fact, must in this second phase of the earth's history have assumed the character of mantle currents. We can prove that at the time the core had grown to its present size the minimum value of the Rayleigh number for a Newtonian viscosity mantle, and therefore the maximum probability, is found for a current distribution according to a third order spherical harmonic. This is also shown by the hatched curve of Fig.IV.1, which gives the inverse value of the Rayleigh number. For the derivation of this hatched curve the writer may refer to HEISKANEN and VENING MEINESZ, 1958, Section 11.4. We see that a fourth order distribution is only slightly less probable.

Fig.IV.1 clearly shows the remarkable good correlation of this hatched curve with the spherical harmonic representation of the earth's topography, which likewise is noteworthy for the regularity of its curve. This is particularly true for the wave of terms between $n = 2$ and $n = 6$, and this in itself points to a physical cause being behind it. The correlation mentioned indicates the cause to be the presence of convection currents in the mantle. Obviously this means that the sialic ur-continent must, during the second phase of the earth's history, have been pulled apart by the above mantle current system. The similarity of shape of the continental coasts on both sides of "split oceans", of which the case of the Atlantic Ocean is especially well known, indicates the great measure of rigidity of the ur-continent at the time of splitting up. The mantle surface may at that time be supposed to have remained fluid, although it may have been covered by a thin more or less rigid layer which did not offer enough resistance to influence the above phenomenon perceptibly.

It is probable that during this pulling apart of the ur-continent the rising mantle currents under the rupture zones caused ridges above them. They formed the mid-ocean ridges, which we shall mention in more detail in the next Chapter. In Fig. IV.1, the ridges are probably responsible for the peaks for $n = 7$, which is shown especially by the ocean curve of this figure. Since it is not shown by the land curve, it must be caused by an ocean-floor feature. It is not present in Prey's spherical harmonic development (see HEISKANEN and VENING MEINESZ, 1958, p.425) and so it must be a large ocean-floor feature that was not known in 1920. This points to the mid-ocean ridges, which have since been discovered through the great number of echo-soundings recently made. This conclusion is also rendered likely by the fact that these ridges are about halfway between the continental slopes, and as the slopes are mainly responsible for terms of the 3rd and 4th order, we can understand that the ridges are giving terms of the double order.

The second phase of the earth's history ended when the mantle crystallized. The third phase, which still lasts, then set in.

5. *The present phase, third phase, of the earth's history; a crystalline mantle*

We know that in the present period the mantle is crystalline; otherwise it is difficult to explain how convection currents can pass through the density transition layer between 500 and 900 km in depth. The crystalline state of the mantle requires the mantle currents to be a more or less continuous deformation of crystalline matter, and so they no longer obey the laws of a Newtonian viscous fluid. The olivine and the spinel must have a certain strength below which a stress deviator[1] can cause only elastic deformations, i.e., deformations that disappear if the stress vanishes. For a stress deviator greater than this elastic limit deformations usually occur proportional to the excess and to the time the stress is applied. If this time is considerable we may speak of "pseudo-flow". In this case we can usually neglect the elastic deformations which remain present as long as the stress operates. Some authors call the phenomenon "plastic flow" (See also VENING MEINESZ, 1956).

The mantle currents have this character of pseudo-flow. They obey different laws from those the viscous mantle currents of the second phase of the earth's history were subject to. By examining Fig.IV.1, we may conclude that probably they are in general distributed according to a fifth order spherical harmonic and that this spherical harmonic is usually of the sectorial kind. The first of these statements seems to follow from the fact that the continental curve shows a prominent fifth order term, which is even larger than the third order term. Since in the present period a great part of the high mountain ranges has a geosynclinal character, we are probably right in assuming that the mantle currents, which by their drag are the cause of the geosynclines, have a fifth order distribution.

This conclusion appears to be confirmed by the fact that the ocean curve of Fig. IV.1 does not show a fifth order term that is larger than the third order term. Since the geosynclines in the oceans are not accompanied by high mountain ranges, this checks with our view that the geosynclines are distributed according to a fifth order spherical harmonic. In the following Section, we shall try to find an explanation of the mantle currents of the present period which have a fifth order spherical harmonic distribution. We can thus also support our second statement about the spherical harmonic being of the sectorial type, which seems to be in harmony with the linear character of geosynclines.

6. A possible explanation of the 5th order spherical harmonic prevailing during the present phase of the earth's history, the third phase

We may probably find an explanation of this mantle behaviour by noticing in Fig.IV.4, that for the present thickness of the mantle of $2900 - 35 = 2865$ km, and a mean outer radius of the earth of 6371.2 km, we can describe ten circles in the

---

[1] A stress deviator represents a state of stress of a volume element that causes a change of shape without change of volume. It is given by five elements, viz. three shear stresses τx, τy, τz and three normal stresses σx, σy, σz, the latter of which together equal zero. It is written:

$$\begin{matrix} \sigma x & \tau z & \tau y \\ \tau z & \sigma y & \tau x \\ \tau y & \tau x & \sigma z = -\sigma x - \sigma y \end{matrix} \qquad (1)$$

According to the criterion of Huber-Hencky, the sum of the squares of the nine constituents of (1) determines the elastic limit. If we denote this elastic limit for the case of uniaxial stress by σ_y, a general stress system exceeds this elastic limit when the sum of the squares exceeds $\frac{2}{3}\sigma_y^2$.

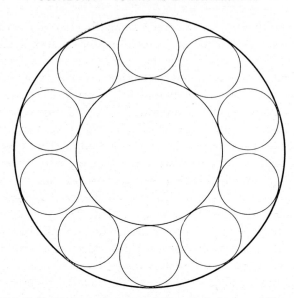

Fig.IV.4. Schematic representation of the currents in a crystalline mantle.

mantle cross-section that are tangential to the inner and outer circles and very nearly tangential to each other. This shows that a mantle-current system is possible, distributed according to a sectorial spherical harmonic of the fifth order, that has the property of having near the equatorial plane of this system a large central part rotating without much deformation. Only the outer parts of these current cells have to adapt themselves to the shape of the cells; we shall call such cells "circular cells". Obviously the equatorial plane of this spherical harmonic system need not coincide with the geographical equator. Because of the rigidity of the mantle matter the property mentioned is evidently important. Because temperature convection is thus possible with a minimum of deformation, we can understand that the half-turn mantle currents take this shape.

The sectorial character of the crustal deformation implies that in a direction at right-angles to the equatorial plane it has a linear character. This checks with the geosynclines that are formed. So we can thus account for the fact that during the present phase, the third phase, of the earth's history, the main effect of horizontal compression in the crust is the formation of geosynclines. During the second phase, on the contrary, the principal effect must have been the pressing together of shields.

We have hitherto dealt with the ordinates of Fig.IV.1 and 2, up to $n = 7$. We shall now briefly discuss the higher orders and continue to do so in Section IV.8. For a more detailed study the reader may refer to VENING MEINESZ, 1961c[1]. It appears

[1] In this paper there is also discussion of the complication of the effects on these systems of current cells of the transition layer in the mantle, dealt with in Section IV. 2.

likely that the further waves of the two upper curves, which must be attributed especially to the continental slopes between continents and ocean floors, and which are best shown by Fig.IV.2, are caused by convection currents in more than one layer above each other, viz. in two, three, four, five, six and seven layers. We may obviously suppose that cells above each other rotate in opposite directions. In the study mentioned it is shown that the convection cells corresponding to this supposition are all circular cells of sectorial character or, in other words, the current cells have a linear character in a direction at right-angles to the cross-section showing the circular cells, in the same way as is the case for the single-cell current hitherto dealt with. It is likely that the effect on the crust is the formation of geosynclines of a smaller cross-section than those caused by the single cell current. The crustal compression belt above the latter has a breadth of 4000 km, the geosynclines here mentioned ought to have a breadth of consecutively 2000, 1333, 1000, 800, 667 and 571 km.

We shall finish our short discussion of the spherical harmonic development of the earth's topography here. In the next Section, we shall study in more detail than hitherto the half-turn currents, which seem to occur during this third phase of the earth's history.

7. *The episodic half-turn currents in the mantle*

Before taking up the subject of the half-turn mantle currents, the question arises whether in a crystalline mantle, in which the temperature increases from the surface towards the bottom, the elastic limit remains the same. If this were not the case and the elastic limit became smaller towards the bottom, the mantle currents might start earlier in the lower part of the mantle than in the upper part. Nothing, however, points to this.

For this problem it is important that in modern research on solid state physics it has been found that up to a certain temperature the elastic limit, indeed, diminishes with rising temperature, but that for several substances, e.g., for magnesium, which is an important constituent of the mantle, it does not continue to do so at still higher temperatures. This agrees with the behaviour in the earth; the temperature at the lower boundary of the oceanic crust is probably given by this transition temperature. For the entire height of the mantle the elastic limit may, therefore, be assumed to be practically constant.

This elastic limit, which has to be overcome before currents can develop, must play a decisive part in causing the mantle currents to assume a half-turn character. Because of this elastic limit the mantle remains stable, although the cooling at the surface brings about a higher density at the surface than lower down. The presence of the transition layer, which likewise causes a potential instability, also remains inactive. The potential instability can increase as long as no horizontal temperature

71

gradient or other effect giving a horizontal pressure gradient is large enough to overcome the atomic forces in the crystals, which determine the elastic limit.

A horizontal pressure gradient that can set into motion the half-turn mantle current may, for example, form in the border area between continents and oceans. This possibility is caused by the temperature difference brought about by the higher content of radioactive matter in the continents than in the oceanic crust. A horizontal temperature gradient may also be brought about by a down-buckled root of sialic crustal matter or by other temperature-affecting circumstances.

The fact that the elastic limit stabilizes the mantle and that, therefore, a secondary phenomenon is required to bring into action the potential instability mentioned, causes the episodicity of the half-turn mantle currents; it would be unlikely that they were exactly periodic. The same is consequently true for the orogenic periods brought about by the mantle currents.

Because of the extremely slow heat conduction, we can assume that during the whole duration of the half-turn current the temperatures, and the densities corresponding to these temperatures, are, practically speaking, carried along by the particles; it is therefore truly called a convection current.

Once set into motion, the velocity of the current will accelerate during the first quarter turn. After that time the subsiding current column contains more or less the mantle matter cooled at the surface, and the rising column the high temperature matter of the deepest mantle layer. The driving force causing the pseudo-flow then has a maximum value and the velocity is likewise at a maximum. During the second quarter turn the current must slow down until, when the half-turn is nearly completed, the pressure gradient can no longer overcome the atomic forces corresponding to the elastic limit, and it comes to a stop. From geological data we can probably conclude that further cooling at the surface may again produce some motion until once more the current stops. It seems possible that such phases of motion may occur more than once before the current finally stops.

At the present time the earth is probably in the second quarter-turn period. From earthquakes and the accompanying crustal motions, from geomorphological indications, and from repeated geodetic measurements and levellings, we know that in many areas crustal movements occur. Mantle currents must, therefore, still be in action. In other areas, such as in the Alps and northern and western Europe, the movements seem nearly, but not quite, finished. In the Alps the crustal compression has diminished sufficiently to allow a rise to great elevation. In southeast Europe, in the Persian, Himalayan and Burmese ranges, in the Rocky Mountains, and in the Andes the earthquakes still indicate great activity in the mantle. In the Indonesian and Japanese archipelagoes and in the other island arcs east of Asia, New Guinea and Australia, the frequent earthquakes, no doubt accompanying crustal deformations, indicate a still earlier phase. The same is probably true for the Antilles.

With regard to the subject of this Section of half-turn convection currents in the crystalline mantle, special attention may be drawn to an early paper by GRIGGS (1939), in which he already discussed the solution of the problem here examined.

8. *Smaller types of mantle currents*

At the end of Section IV.6, we mentioned that the spherical harmonic development of the earth's topography, as represented by Fig.IV.1 and 2, also shows evidence of smaller types of mantle currents, rotating in two, three, four, five, six and seven layers above each other. It is not surprising that smaller current types have occurred. After a half-turn current finishes its course, it leaves a strongly disturbed temperature distribution, i.e., a layer of high temperature on top and a layer of relatively low temperature at the base of the mantle. We have already mentioned that we may expect that the hot core will heat up the lower layer and that the upper layer will lose its high temperature, chiefly by radiation towards the outside. At the beginning this must lead to a strong but fairly shallow downward temperature gradient in both areas, and may be expected to have formed small convection cells, which were probably likewise of the half-turn circular type. In view of the results pointing to the occurrence in the mantle of smaller cells in several layers on top of each other, it appears likely that when these cells form in the upper and lower layers, they are joined by circular currents between. It seems that only in this way can we explain the agreement of the cell sizes with the assumption of continuous columns of smaller cells over the whole height of the mantle, as the curves of Fig.IV.2 seem to show. Because of the probable diminution of the cell sizes downwards, we may infer that it is likely that they are all of the half-turn type. This, however, implies small velocity transitions in the contact zones of adjacent cells in each column. There is no objection to accepting this.

During the period between two large type half-turn current systems the temperature gradients causing these small cells must gradually have extended farther downwards, as well as upwards, and so the size of the cells must have increased. This implies that the number of cells in each column must have diminished. This whole convection mechanism must have accelerated the creation of the conditions needed for a new large size half-turn mantle current system, i.e., the cooling of the upper mantle layer and the heating of the lower layer. If this mechanism had not been there, the time interval between two of these systems, that is between two periods of major orogeny, would no doubt have been considerably longer than the geological facts indicate.

9. *Deep basins in island-arc areas; third arcs*

Most geologists agree in considering it likely that the deep basins in the eastern half of the Indonesian archipelago, e.g., the southern and northern Banda Basins and the Celebes Sea, have recently subsided. Whereas the last great folding activity in the surrounding tectonic arcs probably occurred about 20 million years ago, this subsidence is not older than about 5 million years and may even have taken place 1 or 2 million years ago. Similar views are held for the Caribbean Sea, the Gulf of Mexico, and, according to KUENEN (1936), for the Mediterranean north and northeast of Corsica. We can probably attribute the subsidence of these basins to small-scale convection currents for which the trigger effect needed to release the energy owing to the cooling at the surface was provided by the horizontal temperature gradient resulting from the sial concentration in the surrounding tectonic arc. We may assume that this sial concentration was caused by horizontal compression of the crust.

By estimating the radioactive effects of the excess of sial in the Indonesian arc we find that a time of 15—20 million years is needed for raising the temperature around the sialic root by 80—100° (VENING MEINESZ, 1948, pp.41—45). The corresponding thermal expansion raises the crust by about 100 m, and the resulting stress differences in the mantle are of the order of 12 kg/cm². This is probably sufficient for starting the mantle current. It will make a half-turn, and above the subsiding column a basin must originate. Because of the increase of pressure in the transition layer some olivine will change into spinel, and this considerably increases the subsidence of the basin. A subsidence of 5 km must correspond to an upward shift of the transition layer of $5 \cdot 4.0/0.7 = 28.6$ km. This seems an acceptable supposition, and thus we see that the subsidence of basins to a depth of 5 km can be explained in this way.

The decrease of pressure in the rising current below the tectonic arc around the basin may be expected to cause a lowering of the transition layer there which must be accompanied by a rise of the arc. Because the area of the arc is greater than that of the basin, we may assume that the rise of the arc is less than the subsidence of the basin, which appears to agree with the facts; the arc has probably not risen more than a few thousand metres, and possibly less.

The hypothesis about the existence of these small-scale convection currents below island-arc areas finds further support from the data mentioned in Section III.6 about the more acid matter thrown out by the volcanoes of the inner arc compared with that erupting in oceanic volcanic islands. This was attributed to the sialic down-buckled root of the outer tectonic arc becoming plastic because of the higher temperature of the subcrustal layer in which it was pushed down. This plastic sialic matter was supposed to mix with the matter erupted in the volcanic arc, and this can be explained by the small-scale convection currents here dealt with which rise below the tectonic arc and flow off towards the inside of the arc.

It seems probable that the other young basins in the eastern half of the archipelago, such as the basins of Makassar Strait between Borneo and Celebes, of the

Gulf of Bone between south and southeast Celebes, and of the Gulf of Tomini between north and east Celebes, have also been caused by mantle convection currents. All these basins have depths varying between 2000 and 2500 m. They are, therefore, less deep than those of the former group, but morphologically they have the same character; both groups have flat bottoms and steep sides. It might be that the lesser depth for this second group is caused by their having smaller size; consequently, it appears likely that the mantle currents causing them also have smaller size, and that, therefore, the transition layer is not involved.

Third arcs. In the Banda Sea and in the Caribbean Sea there is clear evidence of a third arc on the inside of the volcanic arc. In the first case it is formed by a ridge, mainly submarine, on which the Turtle Islands and the Lucipara Islands rise above sea level. It may probably be continued towards the Tukang Besi Islands. The origin of this ridge may probably be attributed to crustal compression by the small type convection current to which the Banda Basin is due. This current is obviously short-lived and this agrees with the absence of great folding and earthquakes; it makes only a small topographic feature.

The same can be said of the Aves Ridge in the Caribbean, which is the third ridge in this area; Aves Island is the only feature rising above sea level.

A third instance may, perhaps, be found in a submarine ridge running from the Palau Islands to the northern part of the Nansei Shoto arc. It is represented in the map of this area shown by Fig. V.10.

All these third arcs are situated inside the volcanic arcs at a distance somewhat greater than that between the tectonic arc and the volcanic arc (for further details see VENING MEINESZ, 1951).

10. *Movements of continents relative to the poles and to each other*

It is clear that the system of mantle currents must strongly affect the crust. In Chapter III, we have dealt with the way in which the crust reacts in the continents and in the oceans. We saw that the crustal shortening in a continental geosyncline is limited to a few hundreds of kilometres. This follows from the fact that the sialic crust gives way to the horizontal compression by down-buckling, and that the amount of light crustal matter which can thus be pushed down into the denser mantle is limited. It restricts the crustal shortening mentioned.

In Section III.7, we have already found that for the oceanic geosyncline this limit is not present. Far from the continental borders the sedimentation is slight and so the chemical crust consists practically of only a few kilometres of basalt. The crustal down-buckling in the oceanic geosyncline can, therefore, go on nearly indefinitely. The rigid crust consists mainly of olivine which, if pushed down to a greater depth, gradually assumes higher temperature, melts, and thus can be absorbed in the olivine around. So we may conclude that the rigid crust under the oceans can give way to the horizontal compression much more than the continental crust.

So, the result of these considerations is that the effect of the mantle currents on the crust leads to only slight deformations of the continents in the geosynclinal belts, but that the oceanic crust is more malleable and yields nearly indefinitely.

These results fit in well with the great number of facts pointing to continental drift. To all the arguments given by WEGENER (1929), RUNCORN (1963) in recent times has added the geomagnetic arguments, based on the fact that magnetized rocks indefinitely retain their magnetization, and that, therefore, rocks showing a magnetization that does not fit the geomagnetic field of their present position, must have undergone a transition. Runcorn's studies comprise extensive and numerous research data along these lines, and these data are completely in agreement with Wegener's results which Runcorn, moreover, has further developed, especially by new studies on climatic changes. The mobility of the continents with regard to the poles is obviously included in these views.

It is hardly necessary to add that in this way the hypothesis of mantle currents has found strong support. It may, however, be emphasized that, according to the conclusions reached in this Chapter, continental drift must have been limited to the orogenic periods of the earth's history.

Appendix

FORMULAE FOR $P_n \ldots P_n^p \ldots P_n^n$

Putting $\cos \vartheta = t$, we have:

$$P_n = \frac{1}{2^n n!} \frac{d^n (t^2 - 1)^n}{dt^n} \qquad (1)$$

$$P_n^p = (t^2 - 1)^{p/2} \frac{d^p P_n}{dt^p} \qquad (2)$$

or, introducing (1), by:

$$P_n^p = \frac{1}{2^n n!} (t^2 - 1)^{p/2} \frac{d^{n+p} (t^2 - 1)^n}{dt^{n+p}} \qquad (3)$$

Up to $n = 5$ these formulae give the following results:

SPHERICAL HARMONIC FUNCTIONS P_n, P_n^p, AND P_n^n

Order n	Zonal P_n	p	Tesseral P_n^p	Sectorial P_n^n
0	1			
1	$\cos \vartheta$	..	....	$\sin \vartheta$
2	$\frac{3}{2}(\cos^2 \vartheta - \frac{1}{3})$	1	$3 \sin \vartheta \cos \vartheta$	$3 \sin^2 \vartheta$
3	$\frac{5}{2}(\cos^3 \vartheta - \frac{3}{5} \cos \vartheta)$	1	$\frac{15}{2} \sin \vartheta (\cos^2 \vartheta - \frac{1}{5})$	$15 \sin^3 \vartheta$
3	....	2	$15 \sin^2 \vartheta \cos \vartheta$	
4	$\frac{35}{8}(\cos^4 \vartheta - \frac{6}{7} \cos^2 \vartheta + \frac{3}{35})$	1	$\frac{35}{2} \sin \vartheta (\cos^3 \vartheta - \frac{3}{7} \cos \vartheta)$	$105 \sin^4 \vartheta$
4	....	2	$\frac{105}{2} \sin^2 \vartheta (\cos^2 \vartheta - \frac{1}{7})$	
4	....	3	$105 \sin^3 \vartheta \cos \vartheta$	
5	$\frac{63}{8}(\cos^5 \vartheta - \frac{10}{9} \cos^3 \vartheta + \frac{5}{21} \cos \vartheta)$	1	$\frac{315}{8} \sin \vartheta (\cos^4 \vartheta - \frac{2}{3} \cos^2 \vartheta + \frac{1}{21})$	$945 \sin^5 \vartheta$
5	....	2	$\frac{315}{2} \sin^2 \vartheta (\cos^3 \vartheta - \frac{1}{3} \cos \vartheta)$	
5	....	3	$\frac{945}{2} \sin^3 \vartheta (\cos^2 \vartheta - \frac{1}{9})$	
5	....	4	$945 \sin^4 \vartheta \cos \vartheta$	

Chapter V

THE PATTERN OF MANTLE CURRENTS, OF DEEP OCEAN TRENCHES AND OF VOLCANOES OVER THE EARTH'S SURFACE

1. *Rising mantle currents below the continents and mid-ocean ridges*

As we have already mentioned in Section IV.1, the higher content of radioactive matter in the sialic crust of the continents, compared with the mainly basic crust under the oceans, renders it likely that the mantle temperature below the continents is higher than below the oceans. This must lead to a considerable horizontal temperature gradient from below the ocean crust to below the continent, which can play the part of trigger effect in causing the mantle currents, these currents rising below the border of the continents and subsiding below the adjoining oceans.

For three reasons we must assume that the continental borders are not the only areas below which mantle currents rise, and that this is also the case below the mid-ocean ridges. The first reason is given by the well-known fact that the oceans comprise about 71% of the earth's surface and that, therefore, this enormous area must also overlie rising currents. Since we saw that the parts contiguous to continents are rather likely to have subsiding currents below them, we may assume a tendency of the rising columns of the mantle currents to occur in the middle of the oceans.

A second argument is provided by the frequent finding, during the extensive surveys of the Lamont, La Jolla, and British scientists, of graben on mid-ocean rises, oriented in the longitudinal direction of these ridges. As explained in Section III.4 and 7, this points to horizontal tension in the crust in a direction at right-angles to the strike of the graben, and this must, evidently, mean a mantle-current system rising under these ridges; a subsiding current system below them would obviously mean horizontal compression in the crust. The frequency of volcanoes on the mid-ocean rises, as mentioned towards the end of Section III.7, also points to tension. The fact, likewise mentioned there, that according to gravimetric observations and soundings the Romanche Deep, near the equator in the mid-Atlantic rise, is not a trench but probably a caldeira, is in good harmony with these views.

A third argument is provided by the observation of especially high vertical temperature gradients on the mid-ocean rises. We must realize that the rising mantle currents carry upwards high-temperature matter from the lowest mantle layer and, although part of this heat excess must be absorbed by the transition of the supposed spinel modification to the orthorhombic modification of the olivine, it is unlikely that this would entirely take up the excess of heat. In that case it would be difficult to understand the driving force of the mantle current in the layer of 500 km thickness above the transition layer. In these considerations the extreme slowness of the heat conduction in the mantle plays a dominant part.

The rising current system below the mid-ocean ridges must be responsible for at least part of the rise of these ridges, and perhaps these ridges may even be attributed entirely to this cause. This correlation is evidently brought about by the higher temperature of the rising matter, compared with the subsiding matter; the resulting difference in volume is further enhanced by the transformation in the transition layer of spinel into olivine in the rising column and by the reverse transformation in the sinking column. HESS (1948) is inclined to attribute the entire height of the mid-ocean rises to these causes. By means of a great many soundings during his numerous expeditions in the Pacific he found frequent evidence of truncated cones resting on the sea floor, to which he gave the name of "guyots". This important discovery obviously points to a remarkable mobility in a vertical sense of the Pacific Ocean floor; the guyots can hardly be explained otherwise than by a volcanic origin, followed by the effect of the waves in truncating the volcanic cones and, subsequently, the subsidence of these truncated cones below sea level. In this way Hess made a notable contribution to geophysical research in the Pacific. The writer feels inclined to support his view that the mid-ocean rises are, at least for an important part, due to rising mantle currents below them.

Since Hess' discovery of the guyots, oceanic research has revealed many more of these features, and so it is now possible to form an idea about their distribution. They seem especially to occur on mid-ocean ridges. In a noteworthy paper (HALLAM, 1963), the following summary is given.

The Pacific guyots tend to be confined to limited belts such as the Mid-Pacific Mountains with summits at an average depth of 1500 m (SHEPARD, 1963). A group of sea mounts, including guyots, occurs in the Atlantic north of the Bermuda Rise (depths from 1000—1500 m), and guyots have also been discovered south of the Azores, on the flanks of the Mid-Atlantic Ridge (HEEZEN et al., 1959). Hallam refers to HAMILTON's study (1956) of the guyots in the Mid-Pacific Mountains and agrees with his opinion that isostatic adjustment, oceanic sedimentation, and compaction of sediments under basalt are all of minor importance and cannot account for the main Tertiary subsidence. Nor can the guyots be attributed to a vast addition of juvenile water to the oceans, as suggested by REVELLE (1955).

Considering this evidence of the subsidence of mid-ocean ridges, provided by the presence of guyots, the writer thinks that it can well be accounted for by the hypothesis mentioned towards the end of Section IV.7, according to which the earth at present is in the second half of a half-turn mantle current. This means that the maximum temperature difference between the low temperature of the subsiding current limb and the high temperature of the rising limb, which is located below the mid-ocean ridges, is already past, and consequently the high temperature below these ridges is diminishing and the low temperature adjoining them is increasing. This must bring about a subsidence of the mid-ocean ridges and a rise of the neighbouring ocean basins, which together can explain the evidence provided by the presence on the ridges of guyots. This explanation would, therefore, imply a corroboration of the views mentioned about the cause of these ridges and, at the same time, of the opinion expressed in Section IV.7, that we are at present in the second half of an orogenic period.

In concluding these considerations, the writer may state that probably the mantle currents rise mainly under the continental borders, flowing off towards the oceans, and under the mid-ocean ridges, flowing off towards both sides of these rises. These results give us an important basis for finding the pattern of the mantle currents, which we shall deal with in the next Section. For this purpose we can make use of Menard's map of the mid-ocean ridges, represented in this book by Fig. III.6.

2. *The pattern of the convection currents in the mantle*

In taking up this problem we shall start with the North and South American continents. As has been discussed in Section III.6, the gravity anomalies in the Caribbean archipelago and along the north coast of South America point to a movement of at least the northern part of this continent towards the north-northeast, namely, in an azimuth of about N35°E. It might be that the twisted part of the isthmus in the neighbourhood of Panama has been created by this movement, which in that case must already have been going on for a long time; the total displacement with regard to the North American continent would then amount to about 200 km, and consequently this is probably the result of several mantle-current periods. It would point to a certain stability of the current pattern in successive orogenic periods. The gravity investigations made by EWING et al. (1957), BRUINS et al. (1960), and by VENING MEINESZ (1960), and the results of the soundings are all in harmony with the hypothesis of this relative movement; it is likely to be responsible also for the submarine ridge to the southwest of the isthmus of Panama, which probably marks a crustal fault plane along which this movement can be traced on the Pacific side of the isthmus.

It is likely that the shift affects the whole South American continent. We may suppose that it is caused by a mantle convection current of great size which rises under the submarine ridge indicated in Fig.III.6, and runs from the bend of the Mid-Pacific Ridge, in an azimuth of N120°E, towards the South American coast near Valdivia. This current obviously must affect the continental block and cause wrench faulting along a huge fault plane that, as we may expect, makes an angle of 25° with the mantle current; it is the fault plane that is known to be present

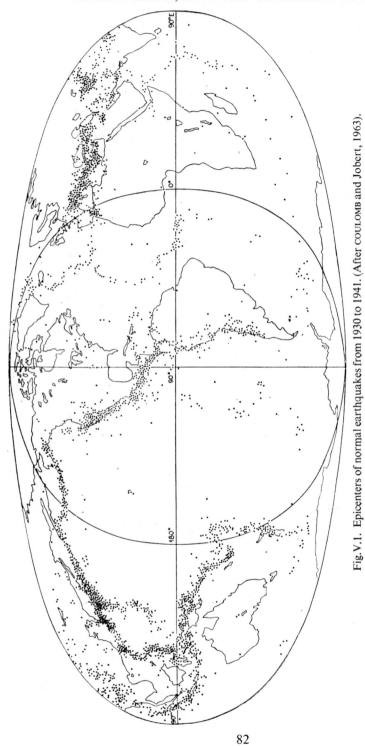

Fig.V.1. Epicenters of normal earthquakes from 1930 to 1941. (After COULOMB and JOBERT, 1963).

in the whole Chilean Andes. The wrench faulting must be accompanied by over-riding, and so we see that this current may also be assumed to be responsible for the formation of the Chilean Andes as well as of the Atacama Trench along the coast. The gravity profiles at about right-angles to the coast, observed by the Lamont expeditions, likewise are in conformity with this hypothesis[1], and so we see that the supposed mantle current can, indeed, explain the great features along this part of the South American coast.

We may no doubt attribute the strong Chilean earthquake of 1960, with its disastrous consequences, which had its focus south of Valdivia, to the crustal processes here described. A right-handed relative movement along the fault plane of about 6 m occurred and obviously the right-handed character fits our hypothesis. The fact that nearly all the Andes earthquakes are located north of this point seems further to confirm our supposition.

The Peruvian Andes make an angle of about 55° with the mantle current here advocated, and this again seems to give corroboration (Fig.V.2). As described in Section III.2, this angle agrees with the formation of a crustal down-buckling and a geosyncline, eventually leading to a high folded mountain range. The geological facts known about the Peruvian Andes do not oppose the view that this part of the Andes has this character. A point in favour is provided by the frequency of volcanoes in the Chilean Andes, practically all centred along the fault plane, and in their absence in the Peruvian Andes, where the down-buckled crustal belt does not allow the passage of magmatic matter. They are again present in the area between Paita and Buenaventura, where the direction of the Andes is in line with the supposed mantle current, and where, therefore, one or more fault planes may be assumed. North of Buenaventura the mountain system consists of several ranges. The coast here has again a north—south direction and in good agreement with this, the gravity profiles at sea at about right-angles to the coast, observed by Otto and Bakker (BRUINS et al., 1960), show fairly strong negative anomalies along this coast, pointing to overriding of the crust in this belt by the coast range belt, while the profiles south of Buenaventura, where the Andes are parallel to the mantle current, do not show any anomalies to speak of.

Farther north the eastern Andes branch continues in the Sierra de Merida, which has an azimuth of about N65°E; it, therefore, makes an angle of 30° with the mantle current. So we may surmise that there will be wrench faulting combined with overriding, and the latter supposition is in line with the conclusion HOSPERS and VAN WIJNEN (1959) reached on the basis of their gravity work there.

The further continuation leads to the Venezuelan coast range with an azimuth of N90°E (Fig.V.3). The angle of 55° made with the mantle current, points to crustal

---

[1] We see that the crustal deformations here dealt with correspond with what has been discussed in Section III.5. For a more detailed treatment of this and also of what follows, the reader should refer to VENING MEINESZ (1964).

Fig.V.2. Structural map of South America. *1* = Brasilian Massif. *2* = Caledonian Brasilids. *3* = Sierras Pampeanas. *4*=Upper Palaeozoic folding. *5* = Jurassic folding. *6* = Not subdivided fold belts of the Andes.(Adapted from BORN, 1932).

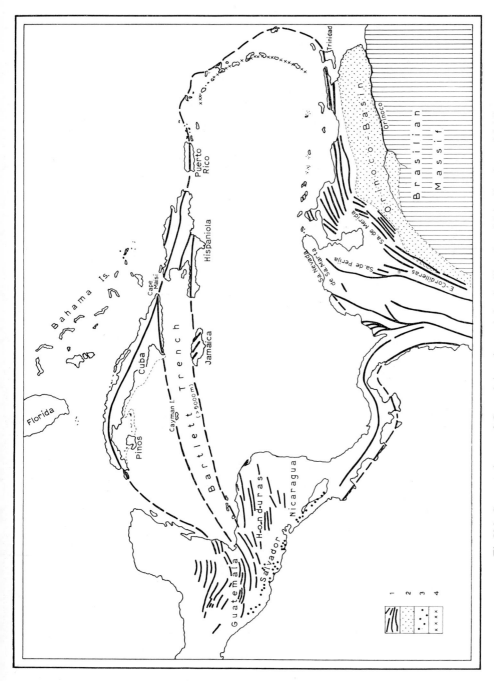

Fig. V.3. Structural map of Central America and the Antilles. *1* = Main directions of folding.
2 = Upper Tertiary. *3* = Volcanoes. *4* = Volcanic-islands arc. (Adapted from BORN, 1932).

down-buckling, geosyncline formation and eventually to a high folded mountain range. This again is in remarkable harmony with the geological facts. We have already mentioned that the same is true for the adjoining Antillean arc up to Cape Maisi.

We may conclude that practically all the geological and geophysical data fit together and point to an enormous field of drag forces exerted by a mantle current with an azimuth of about N35°E. The dimension of this field in the direction of the current amounts to nearly 7000 km. This is a remarkable result, since in Section IV.5 and 6 of the preceding Chapter, we arrived at a probable mantle current distribution with a horizontal dimension of 4000 km. This greater dimension is probably caused by the higher temperature below the South American continent under which the greater part of the horizontal dimension of this current is situated. This higher temperature diminishes the vertical temperature gradient and thereby affects the conditions of motion of the mantle currents. We thus can understand why no subsidence of the current occurs inside the continental area.

Passing to the North American continent (Fig.V.4) we see that only on the western side does seismicity of some importance occur (Fig.V.1). The frequency of earthquakes in California is well known. In Menard's map of the mid-ocean ridges, we see that the Mid-Pacific Ridge is situated at a distance of about 5500 km from the Californian coast, and so we may suppose that mantle currents under that ridge, flowing off towards the American side, will subside at some distance from that coast. This agrees with the fact that the Menard escarpments, which we may surmise to be caused by these mantle currents, do not quite reach up to that coast, although they come near to it. From these facts we can probably conclude that under the oceanic belt along the Californian coast no mantle currents exist parallel to that coast. Whereas the Californian earthquakes are usually caused by relative movements of the right-handed kind along the San Andreas Fault, or along other faults parallel to the coast, we may conclude that the North American continent must be affected by a mantle-current system exerting a drag in a southerly direction. Because of the strong seismic effects attending these movements they may be expected to be accompanied by some overriding, and so we may suppose that the mantle-current system below that continent has a direction converging southwards with respect to the direction of the Californian faults.

Turning our attention now to the other continents, we shall first deal with the Asiatic and Australian continents, and start with the study of the eastern and southeastern parts of Asia, i.e., the island-arc areas, where the great seismic activity points to strong deformation of the earth's crust and, therefore, to the presence in the mantle of active convection currents. Seismic studies of the Indonesian archipelago by VISSER (1949), RITSEMA (1957), VELDKAMP and RITSEMA (1960), H.P.Berlage (see VISSER, 1949, p.128), and others have, in general, confirmed the conclusions, mentioned in Section III.6, which the writer has drawn

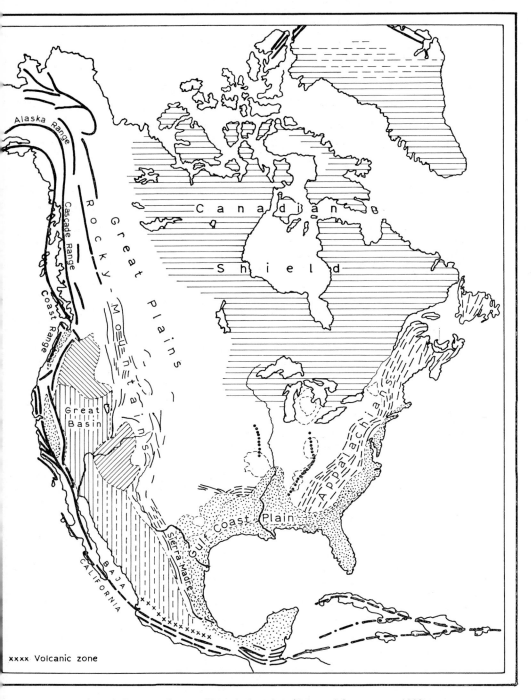

Fig.V.4. Structural map of North America. (Adapted from BORN, 1932).

from studies of the gravity field of that area. He found that the belts of large negative gravity anomalies, as well as other geophysical and geological data, could be explained by a uniaxial compressional stress field in the crust over the whole archipelago in a direction given by an azimuth slowly changing from about N165°E in the western part to about N145°E in the eastern part and N140°E for the Philippine Islands and New Guinea. It is reasonable to attribute this crustal stress field to a large mantle-current system in the same directions.

Extensive seismic and gravimetric research has also been made in Japan. From the results of these observations we can conclude that there also the cause may be looked for in the drag exerted on the crust by a large mantle-current system flowing out from under the Asiatic continent, in this case in a direction given by an azimuth of about N140°E. In view of the fact that between both island arcs we find the Ryukyu or Nansei Shoto arc, and farther east the Bonin—Marianas arc with the Yap and Palau arcs, we may safely assume that over this entire distance the mantle-current system continues, and that its direction is given by an azimuth of about N140°E. Roughly speaking this is about at right-angles to the general direction of Asia's east coast. Considering its great length parallel to the coast, we may safely suppose that this mantle current has a more or less sectorial distribution, and so it is likely that at right-angles to the coast it has a dimension determined by the fifth order spherical harmonic, i.e., about 4000 km. Since we may expect a higher temperature below the continent than under the ocean, we can probably estimate this current system to rise in a belt parallel to the coast at a mean distance of about 2000 km from it, and to subside in the ocean in a belt at about the same distance from the general outline of the coast, i.e., outside or under the island arcs.

North of Japan the Japanese island arc seems to continue in the Island of Sakhalin, also called Karafuto, but from the island of Hokkaido a second arc starts, the Kurile arc, continuing into the Kamchatka Peninsula, and along this arc a trench is present comprising the Tuscarora Deep. Because, however, the direction of this arc and trench does not fit well with the Asiatic mantle-current system, it is questionable whether we can attribute it to that system. It appears more likely that it is due to the drag effect of the current system rising under the row of Emperor Sea Mounts, which in Menard's map is shown to be probably the continuation of the Mid-Pacific Ridge. That this row of sea mounts overlies a rising mantle current is likely since the crustal tension caused by the flowing off to both sides of this current, can explain the row of submarine volcanoes. This row has an azimuth of about N5°W, and so the current flowing off below the crust to the west has an azimuth of N95°W. This checks with the azimuths of the southern and northern parts of the Kurile arc, which are about N60°E and N30°E. So the first makes an angle of 25° with the mantle current and the second an angle of 55°; this points to the first being caused by wrench faulting combined with overriding, and the second by crustal down-buckling.

88

Our hypothesis about the mantle current rising under the Emperor Sea Mounts is rendered still more probable by the fact that the current flowing off below the crust towards the east can explain the Aleutian arc and accompanying trench. It is entirely impossible to attribute this arc and trench to a mantle current flowing out from below Asia.

The most westerly part of the Aleutians makes an angle of 55° with the supposed current and so it may probably be interpreted as a belt of crustal down-buckling; this hypothesis checks with the absence there of volcanoes. It continues in a small but complete arc, likewise without volcanoes, and a longer wing part accompanied by a trench (azimuth of about N110°E), which runs past this small arc and encloses an angle of about 25° with the supposed mantle current. So this part may be interpreted as crustal wrench faulting combined with overriding.

The farther part of the main arc, still accompanied by a trench, appears to be a rift zone, which is more or less in line with the current, but it shows several small parts making angles of about 25—30° with this general direction, and this seems to be in good harmony with our general views about crustal deformation. This whole part is strongly volcanic, as we might expect. Farther east the arc joins the Alaska Range.

Returning to the Indonesian area, we have already briefly mentioned that the mantle-current system dominating the crustal deformations in this archipelago, seems to continue to greater distances from Asia. From the recent exploration of West New Guinea (West Irian) by an expedition under the leadership of Dr. L.D. Brongersma and Commander G.F. Venema of the Royal Netherlands Navy (BÄR and VERSTAPPEN, 1962), we may conclude that the high mountain range of that island is formed by the overriding of the northern crustal block over the southern block along a huge fault plane, and the evidence is favourable to the supposition that this overriding was accompanied by right-handed wrench faulting. This points to the continuation of the mantle current, in an azimuth of N140°E, from the Philippine Islands towards New Guinea, causing this large-scale crustal deformation.

This leads us to suppose that over the full breadth of the Indonesian archipelago the Asiatic mantle current continues. As already mentioned for the mantle current below the South American continent, we may assume that the higher mantle temperature below Australia compared with the adjoining oceans prevents the mantle current from subsiding below it, and so we must suppose it to descend outside the south and east coasts of this continent. Perhaps this current is even strengthened by mantle matter rising below the continent.

These suppositions can satisfactorily explain the mountain formation in Australia. The two highest ranges are the New England Range and the Snowy Mountain Range, forming the highest parts of the Great Dividing Range along the southeast coast. The azimuth of the strike of this range is about N20°E or N200°E and as the azimuth of the corresponding part of the Indonesian archipelago mantle current is about N145°E, the angle enclosed by the two directions is about 55°, which fits our hypothesis of plastic crustal down-buckling. At the southern end of the Australian Alps we find a strike with an azimuth of about N90°E, i.e., likewise with an angle of 55° with the mantle current, and this is also in harmony with this process.

The Grey Range is about parallel to the Great Dividing Range, and so its strike also agrees. Farther west the MacDonnell Ranges have a strike with an azimuth of about N95°E and as the corresponding current azimuth is about N150°E, it is likewise in harmony with the supposition.

The writer found a remarkable result when in 1935 he observed a gravity profile at sea, combined with echo soundings, during his approach to the harbour of Freemantle on the west coast of Australia. Thanks to the collaboration of Prof. A.D. Ross and other authorities he was able to continue this gravity profile inland up to Bruce Rock and Merredin. For details, the reader may refer to VENING MEINESZ, 1948, pl. IV, profile 56. Just off the coast and at the coast this profile shows a cross-section of a belt of negative anomalies of more than —100 mgal at the axis. On land these negative anomalies quickly disappear in going eastward towards the Darling Range.

A tentative interpretation may be advanced by assuming tension in the crust at right-angles to this belt and, consequently, a slipping down of a crustal sialic block along a tilted fault plane; the western slope of the Darling Range may mark the fault plane along which this slip movement has occurred. The writer would emphasize that geological, geomorphological and geophysical conditions preclude the assumption that horizontal compression in the crust causes crustal down-buckling, as is no doubt the case in the belt of negative gravity anomalies in the Indonesian and Caribbean archipelagoes.

The surmise of crustal tension along the Australian west coast seems to be in good agreement with the divergence between this west coast and the direction of the mantle current with an azimuth of about N165°E, that we have supposed to be present in the western part of Indonesia. The writer does not know of another instance of such a phenomenon. He proposes to call it a "half-graben", since the cause of the slipping down is probably similar to that of the subsidence of a graben, i.e., the inclination of the fault plane, which in this case we must suppose to be seawards. The subsidence may be attributed to the readjustment of the isostatic equilibrium of the crustal block on the coast side of the fault plane. This supposition explains the absence of seismic shocks in that area. Two questions, however, remain to be answered: How can we explain that negative anomalies exceeding —100 mgal come into being? And, secondly, how can we explain why the phenomenon is not accompanied by volcanic activity? We shall not attempt here to solve these problems.

We can probably assume that the high ranges of the North and the South Island

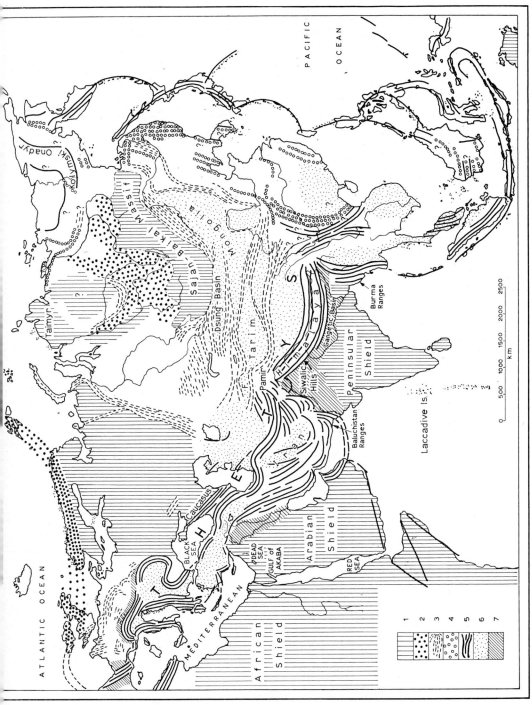

Fig. V.5. Structural map of Eurasia. *1* = Pre-caledonian Massifs. *2* = Caledonian folding. *3* = Upper Paleozoic folding. *4*=Jurassic-Cretaceous folding. *5*=Upper Cretaceous–Tertiary folding *6*=Relatively stable intermediary massifs. *7*=Young border deeps. (Adapted from BORN, 1932).

of New Zealand have originated from the effects of the mantle-current system flowing out from under the Australian continent as a prolongation of the Indonesian current system. They probably make angles of about 55° with the drag forces exerted by this current system. This, however, is certainly not true for the deep Kermadec and Tonga Trenches. They have an azimuth of about N25°E. Although it is difficult to be sure of it, since so few observations have been made in this whole area, it appears likely that they are caused by the mantle-current system rising below the Mid-Pacific Ridge, viz. the Christmas Island Ridge. As is shown by Menard's map this ridge has an azimuth of about N145°E, and this agrees well with the above hypothesis, if at least we assume these trenches to be of the wing type. They make angles of 30° with the current system here advocated.

The whole east Asiatic, Indonesian, Tonga and New Zealand area shows exceptionally strong seismic activity, and this indicates that the mantle currents responsible for this activity must be powerful. In this connection we may note that this entire area borders on the Pacific, and so forms part of the border area between ur-continent and ur-ocean.

We shall now proceed to examine the great Tethys geosynclinal belt, running from Southeast Asia via the Himalaya towards the European Tertiary belt. This latter area includes the Alpine system, the Apennines, the Dinarides, the Atlas and the Sierra Nevada. In part it is as strongly seismically active as the former area.

It gives the impression that this huge belt is a unit, but we shall see that it falls into two units, one east of Asia Minor and one west of it. Fig.V.5, shows that on the northern side it is bordered by the Asiatic and the European continents, on the southern side by old shields which we, therefore, may expect to cover upper mantle areas of relatively high temperature; they are the Indian Shield, often called the Peninsular Shield, the Arabian Shield and the African Shield. We may suppose the continents, as well as the shields mentioned, to be situated over rising mantle currents. For Africa we may especially expect a belt of rising mantle currents below the African lakes, running from Lake Nyasa to the great graben of the Red Sea, the Gulf of Akaba and the Dead Sea, where it joins the Tethys belt. We, likewise, may expect a belt of rising currents below the Mid-Indian Ocean Ridge system with its continuation along the Laccadive Islands, which appears to join the Tethys belt in the Punjab area. As we might expect, both belts of rising mantle currents seem to influence strongly the pattern of the Tethys geosynclinal belt.

For the whole Asiatic part of the Tethys belt the current rising under that continent, which is no doubt the main part of the ur-continent, is dominant with respect to the mantle current rising under the Peninsular shield. As a consequence of this practically all overthrusting during the Tertiary, and also during older periods, occurred from the Himalayan side over the Gangetic Basin side. This is also true for the Baluchistan Ranges in the west and the Burmese Ranges in the east (KRISHNAN, 1960). We can probably assume this same behaviour for the complicated system of ranges and areas in Iran. Here the dominant part played by the Asiatic mantle-current system is clearly shown by the fact that all the arcs are curved towards the south and southwest.

The Himalayan mountain ranges do not seem to be accompanied by Mittel-gebirge in the way which is the case for the Alps. According to the views set out in Section III.3, the Mittelgebirge occur in the area to which the mantle currents move after passing below the principal mountain range, and so they ought to have originated to the south of the Himalayas. Even if the Siwalic Range can be compared to it, the belt is much narrower than for the Alps. We may perhaps

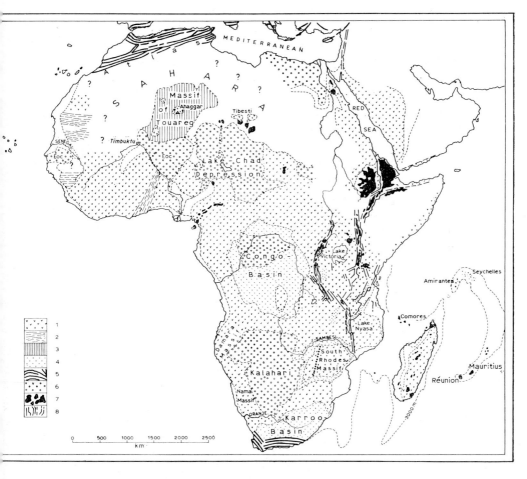

Fig.V.6. Structural map of Africa. *1* = Archaeic-Algonkian basement. *2* = Horizontal older Palaeozoic. *3* = Caledonian folding only. *4* = Karroo; *5* = In the Atlas Mountains: Tertiary folding, in South Africa: Triassic folding. *6* = Tertiary, but alluvial deposits in the Tschad Lake area. *7* = Young volcanic rocks. *8* = East African faults. (Adapted from BORN, 1932).

93

attribute this absence, or minor presence, to the mantle current rising below the Peninsular Shield.

In the European and Mediterranean region the Tethys geosynclinal belt has an entirely different character. No effects point to an appreciable mantle current rising below the European continent. The Caucasus and the Armenian mountains are probably the most westerly ranges brought about by a mantle current coming from the north, although we cannot exclude the possibility that they belong to the Mediterranean system.

In this area we must assume that the mantle currents come from the south, from below the African continent (Fig.V.6). We have already mentioned that below the African Lake belt, which runs northwards from Lake Nyasa, we must suppose the existence of a continuous belt of rising mantle currents, to which the horizontal tension in the crust in a direction at right-angles to the belt may be attributed; this tension causes the graben and the volcanoes characterizing this belt. Towards the north the belt continues in the Red Sea.

But it is likely that in addition to the systems of horizontal mantle currents below the crust, probably flowing off towards both sides of this belt, other currents exist below the African continent, which are responsible for the Atlas Mountains in Morocco, Algeria and Tunisia. These mountain ranges are probably due to a large mantle-current system flowing northwards from a great rising current area below the Sahara, where high temperatures may well be expected. Assuming that the azimuth of the geosyncline corresponding to these ranges has a mean value of about N75°E, we may suppose that the mantle-current system has a mean direction making an angle of about 55° with the mean geosyncline direction, and that it is, therefore, given by an azimuth of about N20°E.

There seems to be reason to suppose that this current system continues below Spain and that it, therefore, is responsible for the tectonic phenomena in the Sierra Nevada, in other mountain ranges of that country, and in the Pyrenees mountain range. From the strikes of these ranges, it seems likely that the azimuth of the direction of pseudo-flow gradually changes to N30°E below the Pyrenees.

It is well known how complicated the Mediterranean and European tectonic pattern is. We shall not enter into details about the great many problems this area raises. We may no doubt assume that the main mantle-current system, revolving through the entire height of the mantle, is and has been accompanied by many smaller current systems – speaking in terms of spherical harmonic analysis, by terms of higher orders – which may be assumed to have been caused by strong horizontal temperature gradients acting as triggers. We may also assume that the effects of the density transition layer in the mantle, i.e., transformations of olivine into spinel and the reverse, have accompanied these small current systems and have led to the subsiding of deep basins, in the same way as has occurred in the deep basin areas in other island-arc areas, as, for example, the Indonesian archipelago.

We also may make the general remark, that probably the mantle current system responsible for the complicated crustal phenomena, comes from the African side. In view of the great volcanic and seismic activity over the Cyclades, Greece and Italy, the latter shown by the map of Fig.V.1, the current system is especially likely to be centred in that belt. It may be that the belt of rising mantle currents, present below the Lake belt of Africa and the Red Sea, continues in this direction. This is in agreement with the volcanic belt over the Cyclades, Sicily, Stromboli and Italy. Another indication in this sense is provided by the tragic earthquake in Skolpje, where a right-handed shear movement occurred along a faultplane in an azimuth of about N10°E (see MERCIER and ROLLET, 1963). As a mantle current rising under Italy and the Adriatic may be expected to flow off below the crust in an azimuth of about N40°E, this would fit the above mentioned shear movement.

This current direction, moreover, is likewise in harmony with the mountain formation in the Balkan, for instance, the Balkan Mountains and the Transsylvanian Alps; both ranges make angles of about 55° with this direction, which check with their character of folded mountain ranges of the type as dealt with in Sections III.2 and III.3.

Further north, this belt of rising mantle currents evidently bends westward and follows the area of the Po valley to stop in the Piedmont region. There can not be any doubt about the strong mantle-current system it brought about flowing north and west below the crust and causing the Alpine geosyncline, viz., the high mountain ranges of the Swiss and French Alps and the Maritime Alps. The angle between the currents and the Alps is about 55° everywhere and this checks with what might be expected in view of the character of a geosyncline belt of the type as discussed in Sections III.2 and III.3.

Further south, it seems likely that the Sardinia—Corsica ridge marks the area where the current system flowing off below the crust to the southwest meets the Atlas—Spanish current system. The latter current system may well be considered responsible for the bending back pattern of the Maritime and Ligurian Alps.

Returning to the formation of the main Alpine geosyncline, there is reason to suppose that the strongest push occurred in the Ivrea zone which faces the highest peaks, the Mont Blanc, the Matterhorn and the Monte Rosa. It is interesting to see that along the inner foot zone in this area a belt of strong positive anomalies occurs with a maximum isostatic anomaly of about + 150 mgal, and reaching from Cuneo to Domodossola (CORON, 1963, fig.II.3, p.2.34).

This has probably been brought about by the inner upward wave of the crust accompanying the great down-buckling belt, which itself lost its strong negative anomalies when in this belt the isostatic equilibrium was readjusted by the rising of the high mountain belt mentioned, and when, furthermore, an important part of the down-buckled root was shorn off by the mantle current system and transported towards the foreland (see Section III.3).

95

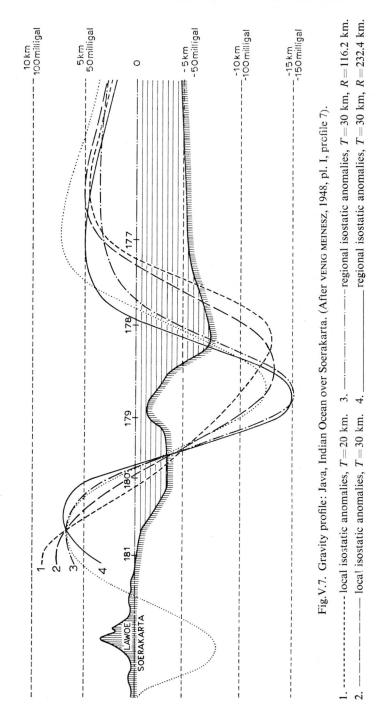

Fig.V.7. Gravity profile: Java, Indian Ocean over Soerakarta. (After VENIG MEINESZ, 1948, pl. I, profile 7).

1. ·········· local isostatic anomalies, $T = 20$ km.   3. ——·—— ——·—— regional isostatic anomalies, $T = 30$ km, $R = 116.2$ km.

2. —— —— local isostatic anomalies, $T = 30$ km.   4. ———— regional isostatic anomalies, $T = 30$ km, $R = 232.4$ km.

So we may assume that this current system continues below the foreland area to the north, northwest and west of the Alpine belt, and in doing so diverges in directions at right-angles to this belt. It must thereby lose velocity, and it must also cause tension in the crust in a direction at right-angles to the pseudo-flow of the mantle currents. According to what has been dealt with in Section III.4, the effect of this tension is the formation of graben and horsts of which the strike must be at about right-angles to the tension. This is shown at the earth's surface in the Upper Rhein graben between the Vosges and the Black Forest, and in the Lower Rhein graben farther to the north. It is likewise found in the surface of the Tertiary and older rocks over the whole area between the Alps and the North Sea. In the southeast of The Netherlands, i.e., in South Limburg, this horst and graben formation leads to the fact that the coal deposits can be exploited on the horsts, but not in the graben, where the depth is too great for mining.

We may close our discussion of the pattern of the currents in the mantle by mentioning that in the southern part of Africa no evidence has been found of the presence of any mantle currents.

3. *The two types of deep ocean trenches and their distribution over the earth*

In Section III.6, we found that there are two types of deep trenches, the central trenches and wing trenches. The first type occurs in the central parts of island arcs and the second in the wing parts, but both types also occur elsewhere. Referring to Section III.6, where the island arcs are dealt with, we may state that the central trenches come into being by the down-buckling of the earth's crust, and the wing trenches by wrench faulting combined with overriding of the crust. Both phenomena lead to the subsidence of a crustal belt, but because the me hanism differs, the two types of trenches have different properties and different histories. Obviously both types are influenced by nearby sediment-providing islands. In this way the central trenches south of Java and north of Puerto Rico are shifted with regard to the axis of the down-buckled belt, and as is shown for the first of the two by Fig. V.7; sediments fill the deepest parts of the down-buckled crustal belt. Although the down-buckled crustal belt must be assumed to be more or less symmetrical, this sedimentation gives an asymmetrical profile to the trench.

The wing trenches are, in principle, asymmetrical. They show the steepest slopes on the side where the overriding by the second crustal block took place. On this side usually an island is found lifted up by this process. On the other side the trench may be expected to taper off in the form of the bending curve of the crust. We find instances of such wing trenches in the Sumatra Trench showing at its southern end a maximum depth of 6200 m (see Fig.V.8, giving a cross-section near to this point), and in the Mindanao Trench having a maximum depth of about 10,500 m; for the

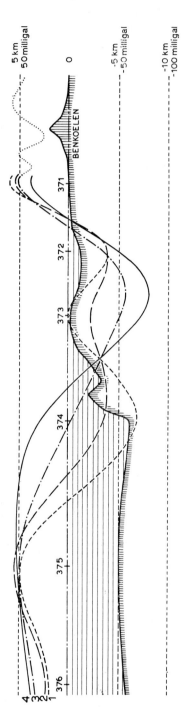

Fig. V.8. Gravity profile: Indian Ocean, Sumatra over Benkoelen. (After VENING MEINESZ, 1948, pl. I, profile 4).

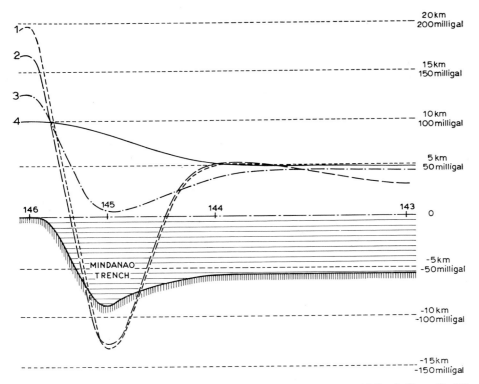

Fig.V.9. Gravity profile: Strait Surigao, Pacific. (After VENING MEINESZ, 1948, pl. II, profile 20).

latter trench the writer has only a cross-section over Surigao Strait somewhat farther to the north than the deepest part of the trench (Fig.V.9).

The three figures also show the isostatic gravity anomaly profiles based on different suppositions about the crustal thickness and the manner of isostatic compensation. Because we must assume that in the Indonesian archipelago the crust is subject to strong horizontal compression, we may expect that the greatest measure of regionality of this compensation is likely to be nearest the truth. This is also shown by the two maps of gravity anomalies, of which the map corresponding to large regionality shows a more regular configuration than the local compensation map.

Examining these figures we see that Fig.V.7 shows a curve that is nearly symmetrical for the down-buckled belt. This again is in favour of the supposition of large regionality; the theoretical treatment of the plastic down-buckling of the crust makes it appear likely that the crustal deformation is symmetrical.

Fig.V.9, gives a cross-section over the Mindanao Trench, which at that spot has a depth of nearly 9000 m. The result of the strongly regional isostatic reduction of the gravity anomalies is remarkable; it seems to fit the physical conditions so exactly that in the anomaly curve the effect of the deep trench has practically disappeared. It may be that for this result it was important that the profile was in line with Surigao Strait, and that we, therefore, may assume that in that area sedimentation in the trench has been small.

Fig.V.8 gives a gravity profile at about right-angles to the west coast of Sumatra near the town of Benkoelen. It differs markedly from the Mindanao gravity profile. It shows a wave of positive anomalies over the Indian Ocean area which exactly fits the low rise in the ocean floor, and this indicates that the rise is not in itself in isostatic equilibrium, but that it is entirely caused by a bending upwards of the un-broken crust through the overriding mechanism in the coastal belt. In this coastal belt we see a fairly large asymmetrical downward wave of the gravity anomaly curve of the regional reduction, and this appears to indicate that here the overriding mechanism involves a pushing of a sialic part of the crust down in the subcrustal layer while in the Surigao Strait profile it must have been a part of the oceanic crust of which the density nearly equals that of the subcrustal layer. This difference checks with the indications given by Fig.V.8 and 9, about the location in the two cases of the crustal fault plane along which the overriding took place. East of Surigao Strait it is situated in the ocean crust and west of Sumatra in the sialic crust which here no doubt extends as far as the row of islands along the Sumatran westcoast (see also VENING MEINESZ, 1948).

For the main subject of this Section, trench formation, the conclusion indicated by Fig.V.8 and 9, remains the same, namely, the asymmetrical character of the wing trenches.

From the preceding details about the two types of trenches it follows that their later histories must be different. When the mantle currents, which formed them, come to a stop, the down-buckled crustal belts comprising the central trenches will readjust their isostatic equilibrium. This causes the trenches to disappear. They are replaced by low submarine ridges of an elevation dependent on the chemical crust in that ocean area; it usually must be of the order of 500—1000 m.

The effect on the wing trenches is somewhat more uncertain, but probably the structures, caused by wrench faulting along the fault planes and by the overriding of one of the two crustal blocks over the other, will remain. However, these struc-tures may gradually be affected by erosion of the higher blocks and by sedimenta-tion on the lower blocks. We need not elaborate here on the different forms these processes can assume, nor the periods involved.

Up to now we have only discussed the trenches occurring in island-arc areas. We shall now examine other trenches. They probably fall into the same two categories, and it is likely that they are caused by the same two processes.

As already dealt with in the beginning of the previous Section, the Atacama Trench to the west of South America comprises two parts. South of Arica it is probably due to wrench faulting combined with overriding, which is brought about by the drag exerted by a mantle current rising below the Pacific Ridge that is running in an azimuth of about N120°E towards the island of Chiloe. Since the strike of the Chilean Andes is about N5°E, this part of the Atacama Trench is probably a wing trench.

The part of this trench to the northwest of Arica may be considered as a central trench. The adjoining part of the Andes is no doubt caused by the same mantle current, which here brings about crustal down-buckling.

The writer does not possess enough data to decide on the character of the trench along the southwest coast of Mexico, Guatemala and San Salvador. It seems likely that we have to classify it as a wing trench; the great shear pattern on the west coast of California and Baja California seems to point in this direction. The gravity profiles which he observed on this part of the west coast of America are in harmony with this view (VENING MEINESZ, 1948, pl. III, profiles 33, 34, 35 and 36).

In the preceding Section we have mentioned that the Tonga—Kermadec Trench may be considered to be a wing trench. This agrees with the straight line pattern of this trench, and it is also in agreement with the results of the important seismic and gravimetric investigations carried out in this area by TALWANI et al. (1959), which do not point to crustal down-buckling. This conclusion is, however, somewhat doubtful because of the fact that we seem to find on one side of the trench an oceanic type of crust and on the other a more or less continental type.

In this connection we may consider the curious Planet Trench to the south of the Bismarck Archipelago and Bougainville Island. It consists of two parts; the western part has a maximum depth of nearly 8300 m and an azimuth of about N115°W, the eastern part a maximum depth of 9140 m and an azimuth of about N135°E. Examining Fig.III.6, we find that these directions indicate central trenches – a conclusion suggested by the fact that they enclose an angle of 110° – caused by a mantle current with an azimuth of N170°W, which corresponds with the current rising under the Mid-Pacific Mountains Ridge (having an azimuth of about N80°W) and flowing off towards the south.

Returning to the trenches in the island-arc areas east of Asia, we shall now make an attempt to attack the difficult problems regarding the complicated area between Asia and the Caroline, Marianas and Bonin Trenches (Fig.V.10). For this area we can make use of the important results obtained by HESS (1948), and also of the conclusion arrived at in the preceding Section about the direction of the mantle currents in this area; over the whole area it probably has the same azimuth of N140°E.

Starting from the northern end, we see that east of the northern half of Honshu we find the Japan Trench with a maximum depth of about 10,000 m. It has the same direction as this part of Honshu, i.e., an azimuth of about N15°E. The southern half of this island makes an angle of about 110° with the northern half, and so it is likely that here we find the central parts of an island arc, which must be due to a

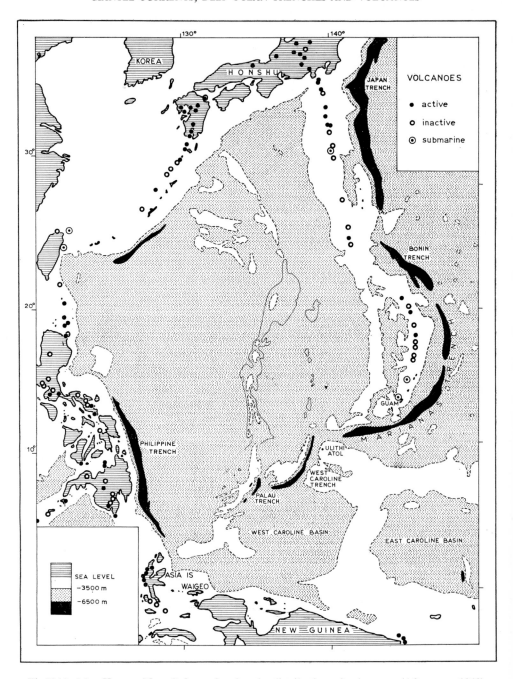

Fig.V.10. Map Korea—New Guinea, showing the distribution of volcanoes. (After HESS, 1948).

mantle current, flowing out from under Asia in a direction bisecting this angle and, therefore, having an azimuth of about N140°E. So this part of the Japan Trench may be regarded as a central trench.

South of the island of Honshu the azimuth of the Japan Trench changes to N168°E and remains the same over a distance of about 1000 km. So it is clear that this part of the Japan Trench has the form of a wing trench; it has changed its character. It may be remarked that the same change occurs in the Indonesian archipelago between the Sumatra and Java Trenches; southwest of Sunda Strait they likewise gradually change from one type into the other. That the change is gradual need not surprise us in view of the fact that it concerns a great crustal structure. The southern part of the Japan Trench shows great depths; the maximum known is about 9400 m. This is situated at great distance from sediment-providing islands, and so we may probably conclude that the trench is not much affected by sedimentation.

South of the Japan Trench a new configuration starts. We see a large arc up to the Ulithi Atoll, which shows the Bonin and Marianas Trenches, then a smaller arc up to the Palau Islands, which is accompanied by the west Caroline Trench, and then a third arc which is likewise accompanied by a trench, but one of smaller maximum depth than the others. There is probably a structural continuation of this arc in the direction of the Asia Islands and Waigeo, but in this area no trenches to speak of have been found[1]. The geophysical interpretation of this whole area, combined with the island ridges and submarine ridges on the inside of the arcs would hardly be possible on the basis of the topography only. For this purpose a judiciously planned gravity survey and further seismic research will be helpful. Since, however, we may be fairly sure of the pattern of the mantle currents responsible for the crustal deformations, the writer may hazard some tentative views about the trenches present.

Because the azimuth of the mantle current is about N140°E, we may expect the central trenches to have azimuths of about N85°E and N195°E; they thus make angles of 55° with the mantle-current system. The azimuths of the wing trenches may be expected to make angles of 25—30° with the current direction, and so they are likely to have azimuths of about N110°E to N115°E or N165°E to N170°E. Examining the arcs mentioned we find that the first two directions are in good agreement with the central parts of these arcs, with this reservation, however, that the two central parts usually merge into each other by means of a continuous curve.

---

[1] "An important indication concerning the tectonic importance of the ridge is given by a gravity profile made in 1929 by the writer across this ridge just north of the Asia Islands, where the depth was 1297 m. In that station a gravity anomaly was found which showed a value of about 120 mgal less than in the stations to the east and west of it. This points to this ridge as belonging to the middle part of a tectonic island-arc, where a crustal down-buckling is taking place" (VENING MEINESZ, 1961a, p.241).

103

We have already mentioned that because of the great dimensions of the crustal deformations such a curve must be considered to be normal. In the greatest arc we clearly see that the two central parts, showing depths of more than 10,000 m, are separated by a less deep part of the trench, which fits our views well. In the two smaller arcs such a separation is also present, although less clearly.

In all three arcs the wing part to the west is missing; obviously it is cut off by the next arc. For the most southerly small arc it is just missing. We may, however, note that the area concerned is not too well surveyed, and so we cannot be sure about the details.

The northern wing trenches, with azimuths of about N165°E, are present in all three arcs. For the largest arc we find the wing trench to extend to a latitude of about 20°N. So, hitherto, we have been able to classify all our trenches, with only one exception, the Bonin Trench, between the latitudes of $24\frac{1}{2}$ and 22°. Similar to what we found in the preceding Section for the eastern part of the Aleutian Trench, the general direction of this trench roughly coincides with the mantle-current direction, i.e., they both have an azimuth of about N140°E, and so this trench does not seem to fit our views about the crustal deformations and trench formation. However, like the Aleutian case, we find that the Bonin Trench is no straight-line formation, but that it consists of parts agreeing with our directions; it shows a bifurcation with a branch running in an azimuth of N166°E and then stopping. So the Bonin Trench does not seem to constitute an exception; it has the character of a wing trench.

We have still to examine the Kurile and Aleutian Trenches. In the previous Section we saw that probably neither of them is caused by mantle currents flowing out from under Asia; it is likely that both are due to a mantle current rising under the Emperor Sea Mounts Ridge and flowing off below the crust to both sides. As has been shown, the northern part of the Kurile Trench seems to have the character of a central trench, while its southern part, as well as the whole Aleutian Trench, is probably a wing trench. The western part of the Aleutian arc is not accompanied by a trench.

We may finish our study on the classification of deep ocean trenches by mentioning that for the southern Antilles the data are not yet sufficient to reach conclusions.

4. *The distribution of volcanoes over the earth's surface*

Everywhere where the cohesion of the rigid crust is sufficiently disturbed to allow magma to reach the earth's surface, we can expect volcanic activity. From this general statement we are in a position to start a systematic discussion of the world-wide distribution of volcanoes or of other volcanic activity.

In the first place we may expect volcanic activity in the areas of horizontal tension

in the crust which we find over rising mantle currents flowing off below the crust towards both sides (Fig.V.11). As was pointed out in Section V.1, we may expect such current systems especially below the mid-ocean ridges, and we find our reasoning confirmed by the fact that everywhere on these ridges there are numerous mountainous formations which we may assume to be volcanoes. Most of them are submarine, but where these formations rise above sea level the islands are volcanic, often in an active state, and this confirms our surmise about the volcanic origin of the formations. In one case the writer had occasion to make gravity observations and soundings above a structure where great depths are found, namely, the Romanche Deep in the area of the Mid-Atlantic Ridge near the equator, and these observations clearly showed this structure to be of the type of a caldeira. Hence in its origin this did not constitute an exception.

The distribution of this great system of volcanoes and other volcanic formations is shown in the map of the mid-ocean ridges represented in Fig.III.6. We see that it comprises the following islands and island groups. In the Atlantic: Iceland, the Azores, Ascension, St. Helena, Tristan da Cunha; in the Indian Ocean: the Mascarenes (Réunion, Mauritius, Rodriguez), the Seychelles, the Maldives and Laccadives, Kergoelen, Amsterdam and St. Paul; and in the Pacific: the Hawaiian group, Christmas Island, the Emperor Sea Mounts, the Tuamotu Archipelago, Easter Island and the Galapagos Islands.

We must, however, also include in this system the volcanoes in the Lake Belt in Africa, the Ethiopian volcanoes, those in the southern part of the Red Sea, and probably the Arabian group to the east of the northern part of the Red Sea. They all overlie a rising mantle-current system.

If the writer is right in his surmise that this rising mantle current continues towards the Alps, we have also to add the volcanoes of the Cyclades, and the Italian volcanoes, Etna, Stromboli, Vesuvius and extinct ones farther to the north.

The system of rising currents which we may expect below the border of continents, especially below the eastern and southeastern border of Asia, is likely only to flow off below the crust towards the border, and so it is not certain that this causes crustal tension to speak of. It may be due to this that no special volcanicity seems to occur there.

A second instance of great volcanic activity is provided by the island arcs, where the inner arc is always formed by a row of volcanic islands or of volcanoes on greater islands. For the part inside the curved belt of crustal down-buckling we can assume that the crust approaching this belt from the inside of the arc must be subject to horizontal tension in the direction of the belt, and so this in itself can explain the volcanic activity. But as has been made clear in Section III.6, this belt is also subject to wrench faulting along a fault plane in the direction of the belt, and this circumstance explains why the volcanoes occur in a row. Exceptionally this may be a double row, as is the case in the Indonesian archipelago, in the Preanger and the Malang-Tengger areas. It is interesting to see that in the same island arc, in the Timor area, where the outer belt, probably because of the shape of the Australian continent, shows a reversed curve, the inner arc is no longer volcanic; it is also straight in this area. This strongly points in the direction of our suppositions regarding the volcanicity of the inner arc and its faultplane character. Another point in favour of it is found in the fact that in other island arcs it is always the inner arc which is volcanic.

In no island-arc area is the tectonic arc volcanic. Obviously this is caused by the fact that in this arc the crust is subject to down-buckling under great horizontal compression. Clearly this state of the crust does not allow the overcoming of crustal cohesion needed for volcanic activity.

It is important to notice in our map of the Indonesian archipelago (Fig.II.1), that on the wings of the arc, the inner arc is also volcanic. However, examining the Sumatra area, we get the impression that the belt, where the wrench faulting combined with overriding took place, does not allow sufficient disruption of the crustal cohesion for volcanic activity, and that this, therefore, occurs in a parallel fault belt inside the island. As mentioned in Section III.3, p.39, movements along such a fault plane were found to occur during an earthquake; a re-measuring of the triangulation revealed them.

The contribution provided by the island-arc areas to the volcanicity at the earth's surface is well known. It is not necessary to enlarge on it further.

There is no doubt that other areas of wrench faulting combined with overriding are likewise subject to strong volcanicity. We may mention here the Chilean Andes which, according to the views expressed in Section V.2, the writer attributes to the mantle current rising under the branch of the Mid-Pacific Ridge running towards Chiloé Island. This current flows off below the crust in an azimuth of about N30°E, and causes wrench faulting combined with overriding which leads to the formation of the Andes and the accompanying deep trench. Farther north, in Peru, the strike of the Andes changes to a direction which makes an angle of about 55° with the mantle current, and so we may assume that here the crustal deformation brought about by this current has the character of plastic down-buckling and geosyncline formation, thus leading to this part of the Andes with the adjoining trench. It is consistent with the views here advocated that the Chilean part of the Andes is strongly volcanic and that the Peruvian part is not volcanic at all.

A great many volcanic islands in the Pacific may no doubt be attributed to the horizontal mantle currents flowing off below the crust from the area of the rising current-system under the Mid-Pacific Ridge. We may mention the Tonga Islands, the Fiji Islands, the Society Islands, the Cook Islands, the Phoenix Islands, the Gilbert Islands and the Caroline Islands. Without further investigations it is difficult to say whether the Solomon Islands, the New Hebrides group and the volcanoes on the Northern Island of New Zealand are all due to the great mantle-current system flowing out from under Asia and causing the crustal deformations in the Indonesian archipelago, or whether part of them may be attributed to the horizontal mantle-current system connected with the current system rising below the Mid-Pacific Ridge. It is rather likely that these two great mantle-current systems are not independent of each other, but that they join together in their subsiding areas.

Lastly, we may mention the volcanoes of the Kurile—Kamchatka and Aleutian arcs, which we have already discussed in Section V.2. According to the results obtained there, we may attribute these volcanoes to the wrench faulting caused by the horizontal currents flowing off to both sides from the current system rising under the Emperor Sea Mounts.

We now return to the volcanoes on the western side of the American continents and to the north of Peru. Successively we have the Ecuador—South Colombia group, the Central American group, the Mexican group, the New Mexico group (more inland), the Cascade group, and the Alaska group.

The Ecuador—South Colombia group of volcanoes may probably be attributed to the general movement of the South American continent to the north-northeast, i.e., in an azimuth of about N35°E. This movement relative to the crustal block to the west-northwest of the shear zone, which runs from Panama to the area of Cape Maisi (southeast Cuba), may be expected to have a loosening effect on the crust in the area here mentioned.

The Central American group might perhaps tentatively be accounted for by a mantle-current system rising under the mostly submarine ridge, indicated in Fig. III.6, which runs from the Mid-Pacific Ridge towards Central America. If it continues under Central America, it would explain horizontal tension in the crust in that area, and obviously this might lead to volcanic activity. A second branch of this ridge, suggested by Menard's map, might in the same way account for the Mexican volcanoes.

For the last three groups we have to study the mantle current distribution below and in the area of the North American continent. As we mentioned in Section V.2, we expect the presence below that continent of a mantle-current system in a southerly direction, which converges towards the direction of the Californian faults, i.e., the San Andreas Fault and other parallel faults. The volcanic activity in the Yellowstone Park and in the New Mexico area seems to suggest a certain velocity increase of this current system in an eastward direction, which causes tension effects. The writer may also refer here to a recent paper by WISE (1963), in which he proposes "to attribute the spreading pattern of this mountain system to right-lateral distortion of several hundred miles from Palaeozoic through modern times across a 300-mile-wide zone from the Colorado Plateau to the Pacific Northwest". Besides the spreading pattern of the mountain system, the hypothesis can not only account for the volcanic activity mentioned, but also for the Cascade group of

111

volcanoes, which is situated in an area where the direction of the coast and of the Cascade Range have an azimuth of about N195°E. This direction causes a divergence, in looking south, between the current direction and the Cascade Range, and it is clear that this may cause crustal tension in a west—east direction.

The Alaska group of volcanoes seems more or less to consist of two parts. The western part is a continuation of the Aleutian arc, of which the volcanicity can be attributed to the mantle current to which this arc appears to be due, that is the current flowing off in an eastward direction from below the Emperor Sea Mounts row (see Section V.2). The eastern part of the Alaskan volcanoes may well be caused by some deformation of this part of the North American continent, brought about by the movement in a southerly direction of the continent as a whole, which is not quite followed by a similar movement of the Alaskan part of it; we need not be surprised that no mantle current of any consequence is rising below it. This must lead to a bending and, therefore, to a tendency towards horizontal tension along the southern belt. Hence there might be a reason for the volcanic activity.

On March 27, 1964, an extremely severe earthquake occurred in the Anchorage area (Alaska); the intensity of this earthquake exceeded even that of the San Francisco earthquake of 1906. The subsidence of the main street of Anchorage over a fairly great length to a depth of the order of 10 ft. points to tension in the crust; this probably corroborates the above view. Anchorage is situated in the prolongation of the San Andreas fault; thus, it is likely that a crustal movement took place caused by the same mantle current that transports the North American continent in a southerly to south-southeasterly direction. The slight shocks registered on the Louisiana coast seem to be in harmony with this supposition.

We shall now examine the part of the European continent to the north and west of the Alps. In Section V.2, we have already mentioned the manifold evidence indicating horizontal crustal tension in this area in a direction at right-angles to the current system, which diverges from the Alps to the west, northwest and north. We called attention to the Upper and Lower Rhein graben, which was accompanied by volcanic activity, now extinct. As evidence of past volcanicity we may, for example, mention the Siebengebirge, to the southeast of Bonn. Evidence of quite recent volcanic activity is provided by the Eifel Mahren, where little round lakes represent old craters. We may likewise mention the area of the Plateau Central in France where the evidence of past volcanicity is well known. The few examples mentioned could be multiplied indefinitely. Whether in this connection we should call attention to extinct volcanicity in Scotland seems uncertain; it might also have been caused by the mantle currents responsible for the great relative displacements along the Great Glen Fault.

We shall now briefly examine the volcanicity in the three Atlantic island groups of the Canaries, of the Cape Verde Islands, and of the row of volcanic islands from Annobom to Fernando Po. It seems reasonable to attribute the first two groups to the diverging mantle current rising under West Africa, which, in Section V.2, we have already mentioned as being responsible for mountain formation in Spain and Portugal. This divergence must have a similar effect to that mentioned for the area between the Alps and the west and northern coasts of Europe; it must bring about horizontal tension in the crust at right-angles to the direction of flow of the mantle currents.

For the origin of the third row of volcanic islands we have probably to look for a branch of rising mantle currents joining the belt below the Mid-Atlantic Ridge; there is evidence of a submarine ridge in this direction.

As it is well known, volcanoes likewise occur in the Antarctic continent, but the data about this continent are not yet sufficient to come to any conclusions about the volcanicity.

Finally the writer may emphasize that the discussion of the earth's volcanic activity given in this Section is far from complete.

5. *Mountain formation on the continents*

With regard to the high mountain ranges we may distinguish two main types, the geosynclinal ranges and the wrench-faulted ranges. Following the same line as we adopted in Section V.3, for the trenches, we shall designate the geosynclinal ranges as "central ranges" and the wrench-faulted ranges as "wing ranges". This refers to the way such structures are distributed in island arcs. The central ranges may be expected to make angles of about 55° with the direction of the mantle currents to which they are due, and the wing ranges 25—30°.

Central ranges may in a certain area continue as wing ranges and vice versa. As an example, the writer may point to the Peruvian Andes, which south of Arica continue in the Chilean Andes. The first may be assumed to be a central range, the second a wing range.

According to their origin by strong horizontal compression of the rigid crust, the central ranges may show considerable folding and overthrusting. For the wing ranges the relative movement of the two crustal blocks on both sides of the range is mainly right- or left-handed wrench-faulting shear, which is combined with over-riding. So the compression at right-angles to the range is less and great overthrusting cannot be expected. On the other hand, the wing ranges originate by shear along a huge fault plane through the entire crust, and this implies that this type of range may show large volcanoes, probably often on a more or less straight row which marks the fault plane. The central ranges may be expected to be free from recent volcanoes. This difference in volcanic activity is, indeed, shown by the example we mentioned; the Peruvian Andes show no volcanoes and the Chilean Andes are marked by a great number of large ones.

We may, perhaps, suppose that besides these two types of high ranges, there is still another possibility of rows of high volcanoes, i.e., when crustal shear occurs along a fault plane more or less in the direction of the mantle currents, which then must be expected to show a change of velocity in a direction at right-angles to this plane. In this case we must assume that the high topography has an entirely volcanic origin.

Besides the high ranges hitherto mentioned we may consider the topography caused by crustal tension. As noted in Section III.4, we may in this case expect the formation of graben and horsts. This topography in itself may be assumed not to lead to mountains and ranges higher than about 1500 m, but it may be expected to be accompanied by high volcanoes as is the case for the Lake Belt through East Africa.

From the last two cases we may conclude that volcanic topography and volcanic ranges may make all kinds of angles with the direction of the mantle currents; they do not allow a classification into central and wing ranges.

We now come to the Mittelgebirge topography. As was mentioned in Section III.3, this topography may be assumed to be caused by the lifting up of the crust by sialic root material which is transported from the areas of high folded mountain ranges to the foreland by the mantle currents. We may assume that during this lifting process, the rivers coming from the high mountain ranges cut their beds in this lifted area and may continue to do so. We thus get a topography which is mainly due to lifting and erosion, although the mantle currents may cause some folding. In the part of Europe between the Alps and the coasts, these mantle currents diverge and thereby lose velocity and so we may expect that their drag is not enough to cause much crustal folding.

There is still another possibility of the lifting up of the crust, which may lead to erosion and the formation of topography, viz. chemical changes in the crust or substratum which affect the mean density. The writer is not sure whether such phenomena occur in a measure which leads to topography of some general importance.

REFERENCES

AHLBURG, J., 1913. Versuch einer geologischer Darstellung der Insel Celebes. *Geol. Paläontol. Abhandl.*, 12 : 172 pp.

AIRY, G.B., 1855. On the computation of the effect of the attraction of mountain masses as disturbing the latitude. *Phil. Trans. Roy. Soc., London, Ser. B*, 145 : 101—104.

ANDERSON, E.M., 1951. *The Dynamics of Faulting*. Oliver and Boyd, Edinburgh, 206 pp.

ARGAND, E., 1916. Sur l'arc des Alpes Occidentales. *Eclogae Geol. Helv.*, 14 : 145—191.

BÄR, C.B. and VERSTAPPEN, H.TH., 1959. Geological results of the Star Mountains (Sterrengebergte) expedition, *Nova Guinea*, 10 *(Geol., 4)* : 39—99.

BÄR, C.B. and VERSTAPPEN, H.TH., 1962. Some volcan tectonic depressions on Sumatra. Origin and mode of development. *Koninkl. Ned. Akad. Wetenschap., Proc., Ser. B.*, 64 : 428—443.

BERNAL, J.D., 1936. Hypothesis on 20° discontinuity. *Observatory*, 59 : 268.

BIJLAARD, P.P., 1935. Beschouwingen over de knikzekerheid en de plastische vervormingen van de aardkorst in de Indische Archipel. *Ingr. Ned. Indië*, 11 : 135—156 (Dutch with German summary).

BIJLAARD, P.P., 1936. Théorie des déformations, plastiques et locales par rapport aux anomalies de la gravité, aux fosses océaniques, aux géosynclinaux, etc. *Intern. Geophys. Geodet. Union, Rept. Congr., Edinburgh, 1936, 6th Gen. Assembly*.

BIRCH, F., 1942. Thermal conductivity of rocks. In: F. BIRCH, J.F. SCHAIRER and H.C. SPICER, *Handbook of Physical Constants*. *Geol. Soc. Am. Spec. Paper*, 36 : 251—258.

BORN, A., 1932. Der geologische Aufbau der Erde. In: B. GUTENBERG (Herausgeber), *Handbuch der Geophysik*. Borntraeger, Berlin, 2(2) : 565—866.

BOUGUER, P., 1749. *La Figure de la Terre*. Paris, 364 pp.

BOWEN, N.L., 1928. *The Evolution of Igneous Rocks*. Princeton Univ. Press, Princeton, N.Y., 334 pp.

BROUWER, H.A., 1927. Verslag van de geologische excursie naar de Zwitserse Jura en Alpen, van 28 Aug. tot 20 Sept. 1927. *Mijnb. jaarb.*, 1926—1928 : 1—97.

BRUINS, G.J., DORRESTEIN, R., VESSEUR, H.J.A., BAKKER, G. and OTTO, L., 1960. Atlantic, Caribbean and Pacific cruises. In: G.J. BRUINS (Editor), *Gravity Expeditions at Sea, 1948—1958. Publ. Neth. Geodetic Comm.*, 5 : 11—47.

BULLARD, E.C., 1936. Gravity measurements in East Africa. *Phil. Trans. Roy. Soc., London, Ser. A*, 235 : 445—531.

BULLARD, E.C., 1948. The figure of the earth. *Monthly Notices Roy. Astron. Soc., Geophys. Suppl.*, 5(6) : 186—192.

CLAIRAUT, A.C., 1743. *Théorie de la Figure de la Terre*, 249 pp.

CORON, S., 1963. Aperçu gravimetrique sur les Alpes Occidentales. Dans H. CLOSS et Y. LABROUSTE (Rédacteurs), Seismologie, Année Géophysique Internationale, Participation francaise. *Centre Natl. Rech. Sci., Sér.*, 12 (2) : 31—37.

COULOMB, J., 1952. *La Constitution physique de la Terre*. Michel, Paris, 284 pp.

COULOMB, J. and JOBERT, G., 1963. *The Physical Constitution of the Earth*. Oliver and Boyd, Edinburgh, 328 pp.

DARWIN, G.H., 1899. The theory of the figure of the earth, carried to the second order of small quantities. *Monthly Notices Roy. Astron. Soc.*, 60 : 82—124.

DE SITTER, W., 1924. On the flattening and the constitution of the earth. *Bull. Astron. Inst. Neth.* 55 : 97—108.

DU TOIT, A.L., 1937. *Our Wandering Continents. A Hypothesis of Continental Drifting*. Oliver and Boyd, Edinburgh, 366 pp.

DUTTON, C.E., 1889. On some of the greater problems of physical geology. *Bull., Wash. Phil. Soc., Section B*, 11 : 51—64. Reprinted 1931, in: *Physics of the Earth II – Bull. Natl. Res. Council (U.S.)*, 78 : 201—211.

EWING, M., WORZEL, J.L. and SHURBET, G.L., 1957. Gravity observations at sea in U.S. submarines Barracuda, Tusk, Conger, Argonaut and Medregal. In: *Gedenkboek Vening Meinesz – Verhandel. Koninkl. Ned. Mijnbouwk. Genoot., Geol. Ser.*, 18 : 49—116

GRIGGS, D., 1939. A theory of mountain-building. *Am. J. Sci.*, 2 : 611—650.

GUTENBERG, B., 1945. Amplitudes of surface waves and magnitudes of shallow earthquakes. *Bull.Seismol.Soc.Am.*, 35: 3—12.

GUTENBERG, B., 1951. *Internal Constitution of the Earth*, 2nd. ed. Dover-Publ., 439 pp.

HAFNER, W., 1951. Stress distributions and faulting. *Bull. Geol. Soc. Am.*, 62 : 373—398.

HALLAM, A., 1963. Major epeirogenic and eustatic changes since the Cretaceous and their possible relationship to crustal structure. *Am. J. Sci.*, 261 : 397—423.

HAMILTON, E.L., 1956. Sunken islands of the Mid-Pacific Mountains. *Geol. Soc. Am., Mem.*, 64 : 1—97.

HARRISON, J.C., 1955. An interpretation of gravity anomalies of the Eastern Mediterranean. *Phil. Trans. Roy. Soc. London, Ser. A*, 248 : 283—325.

HARRISON, J.C., BROWN, G.L. and SPIESS, F.N., 1957. Gravity measurements in the northeastern Pacific Ocean. *Trans. Am. Geophys. Union*, 38: 835—840.

HAYFORD, J.F. and BOWIE, W., 1912. Effect of topography and isostatic compensation upon the intensity of gravity. *U.S. Coast and Geodetic Survey, Spec. Publ.*, 10.

HEEZEN, B.C., THARP, M. and EWING, M., 1959. The floors of the Oceans. 1. The North Atlantic. *Geol. Soc. Am. Spec. Papers*, 65 : 122 pp.

HEISKANEN, W.A., 1938. New isostatic tables for the reduction of the gravity values calculated on the basis of Airy's hypothesis. *Publ. Isos. Inst. I.A.G. (Helsinki)*, 2.

HEISKANEN, W.A. and VENING MEINESZ, F.A., 1958. *The Earth and its Gravity Field*. McGraw–Hill, New York, 470 pp.

HESS, H.H., 1948. Major structural features of the western North Pacific: an interpretation of H.O. 5485, bathymetric chart, Korea to New Guinea. *Bull. Geol. Soc. Am.*, 59 : 417—445.

HOSPERS, J. and VAN WIJNEN, J.C., 1959. The gravity field of the Venezuelan Andes and adjacent basins. *Verhandel. Koninkl. Ned. Akad. Wetenschap., Sect. I.*, 23 (1) : 1—95.

KING HUBBERT, M., 1951. Mechanical basis for certain familiar geologic structures. *Bull. Geol. Soc. Am.*, 62 : 355—372.

KRISHNAN, M.S., 1960. *Geology of India and Burma*. 4th ed. Higginbothams, Madras, 604 pp.

KUENEN, PH.H., 1936. The negative isostatic anomalies in the East Indies. *Leidse Geol. Mededel.*, 8 : 169—214.

KUENEN, PH. H. and HUMBERT, F.L., 1964. Bibliography of turbidity currents and turbidites. In: A.H. BOUMA and A. BROUWER (Editors). *Turbidites*. Elsevier, Amsterdam, pp. 222—246.

MEIJERING, J.L. and ROOYMANS, C.J.M., 1958. On the olivine-spinel transition in the Earth's mantle. *Koninkl. Ned. Akad. Wetenschap., Proc., Ser. B*, 61 (5) : 333—344.

MENARD, H.W., 1955. Deformation of the northeastern Pacific and the west coast of North America. *Bull. Geol. Soc. Am.*, 66 : 1149—1198.

MENARD, H.W., 1958. Development of median elevations in ocean-basins. *Bull. Geol. Soc. Am.*, 69 : 1179—1185.

MENARD, H.W., 1959. Geology of the Pacific sea floor. *Experientia (Switzerland)*, 15(6) : 205—213.

MERCIER, J. and ROLLET, M., 1963. Le séisme de Skopje (Macedoine, Yougoslavie) et ses relations avec la tectonique. *Compt. Rend.*, 1963 : 2134—2137.

MULLER, J.J.A., 1895. De verplaatsing van enige triangulatie-pilaren in Tapanoeli (Sumatra). *Verhandl. Koninkl. Akad. Wetenschap., Sect. I*, 3(2) : 3—26.

POINCARÉ, H., 1900. *Figures d'Équilibre d'une Masse Fluide*. Paris.

PRATT, J.H., 1855. On the attraction of the Himalaya Mountains and on the elevated regions beyond upon the plumbline in India. *Phil. Trans. Roy. Soc. London, Ser. B*, 145 : 53.

PREY, A., 1922. Darstellung der Höhen- und Tiefen- verhältnisse der Erde durch eine Entwicklung nach Kugelfunktionen bis zur 16. Ordnung. *Nachr. Akad. Wiss. Göttingen, Math.–Physik. Kl.*, 11 (1) : 1—29.

READ, H.H., 1955. Granite series in mobile belts. In: A. POLDERVAART (Editor), *The Crust of the Earth* – Geol. Soc. Am., Spec. Papers, 62 : 409—429.

REVELLE, R., 1955. On the history of the Oceans. *J. Marine Res.*, 14 : 446—461.

RITSEMA, A.R., 1957. On the use of transverse waves in earthquake mechanism studies and the direction of fault displacement in southeast Asian earthquakes. *Lembaga Meteorol. Geofis.*, 52.

RUNCORN, S.K. (Editor), 1963. *Continental Drift*. Acad. Press, New York, 338 pp.

116

REFERENCES

SHEPARD, F.P., 1963. *The Earth beneath the Sea.* Johns Hopkins Univ. Press, Baltimore, Md., 2nd ed., 275 pp.

STAUB, R., 1924. Der Bau der Alpen. *Beitr. Geol. Karte Schweiz,* 52.

STOKES, G.G., 1849. On the variation of gravity and the surface of the earth. *Trans. Cambridge Phil. Soc.,* 8 : 672—695.

TALWANI, M., WORZEL, J.L. and EWING, M., 1961. Gravity anomalies and crustal section across the Tonga Trench. *J. Geophys. Res.,* 66 : 1265—1278.

TALWANI, M., WORZEL, J.L. and LANDISMAN, M., 1959. Rapid gravity computations for two-dimensional bodies with application to the Mendocino submarine fracture zone. *J. Geophys. Res.,* 64 (1) : 49—59.

TAYLOR, F.B., 1910. Bearing of the Tertiary Mountain Belt on the Origin of the Earth's Plan. *Bull. Geol. Soc. Am.,* 21 : 179—226.

TISSERAND, F., 1891. *Traité de Mécanique Terrestre Céleste.* Gauthier-Villars, Paris, 2 : Chapt. 15.

UMBGROVE, J.H.F., 1932. Het Neogeen in den Indischen Archipel. *Tijds. Koninkl. Ned. Aardrijksk. Genoot.,* 49 : 769—833.

UMBGROVE, J.H.F., 1933. Verschillende typen van Tertiaire Geosynclinalen in den Indischen Archipel. *Leidse Geol. Mededel.,* 6 : 33—43.

UMBGROVE, J.H.F., 1934. The relation between Geology and Gravity Field in the East Indian archipelago. In: *Gravity Expeditions at sea – Publ. Neth. Geodetic Comm., 1923—1932,* II Chapt. VI—VII : 140—184.

UMBGROVE, J.H.F., 1947. *The Pulse of the Earth.* Nijhoff, den Haag, 358 pp.

VELDKAMP, J. and RITSEMA, A.R., 1960. Fault plane mechanisms of southeast Asian earthquakes. *Verhandel. Koninkl. Ned. Meteorol. Inst.,* 76 : 1—63.

VENING MEINESZ, F.A., 1942. The equilibrium figure of the earth and the indirect or Bowie reduction. *Koninkl. Ned. Akad. Wetenschap., Proc., Ser. B.,* 45 : 3—10.

VENING MEINESZ, F.A., 1946. The indirect isostatic or Bowie reduction and the equilibrium figure of the Earth. *Bull. Géodésique, N. Sér.,* 1 : 33—107.

VENING MEINESZ, F.A., 1948. *Gravity Expeditions at Sea. – Publ. Neth. Geodetic Comm., 1948,* 4 : 1—233.

VENING MEINESZ, F.A., 1951. A third arc in many island-arc areas. *Koninkl. Ned. Akad. Wetenschap., Proc., Ser. B,* 54(5) : 432—442.

VENING MEINESZ, F.A., 1955. Plastic Buckling of the Earth's Crust: The Origin of Geosynclines. In: A. POLDERVAART (Editor), *The Crust of the Earth – Geol. Soc. Am., Spec. Papers,* 62 : 319—330.

VENING MEINESZ, F.A., 1956. Elasticity and plasticity. *Appl. Sci. Res. Sect. A,* 6 : 205—225.

VENING MEINESZ, F.A., 1959. The outside gravity field up to great distance from the earth. *Koninkl. Ned. Akad. Wetenschap., Proc., Ser. B,* 62 : 109—114.

VENING MEINESZ, F.A., 1960. Preface. In: G.J. BRUINS (Editor), *Gravity Expeditions at Sea, 1948—1958. Publ. Neth. Geodetic Comm.,* 1960, 5 : 5.

VENING MEINESZ, F.A., 1961a. Orogeny in the New Guinea, Palao, Halmaheira area; geophysical conclusions. *Koninkl. Ned. Akad. Wetenschap., Proc., Ser. B,* 64 (2) : 240—244.

VENING MEINESZ, F.A., 1961b. Convection currents in the mantle of the earth. *Koninkl. Ned. Akad. Wetenschap., Proc. Ser. B.,* 64 (4) : 501—511.

VENING MEINESZ, F.A., 1961c. Continental and ocean-floor topography, mantle convection currents. *Koninkl. Ned. Akad. Wetenschap., Proc. Ser. B,* 64(4) : 512—527.

VENING MEINESZ, F.A., 1964. Interpretation of gravity anomalies on the west coast of South America and in the Caribbean. *Publ. Neth. Geodetic Comm.,* Delft, in press.

VÉRONNET, A., 1912. Rotation de l'ellipsoide hétérogène et figure exacte de la terre. *J. Math. Phys. Appl.,* 7.

VISSER, S.W., 1949. *Seismologie,* Noorduyn, Gorinchem, 160 pp.

WEGENER, A., 1929. *Die Entstehung der Kontinente und Ozeane.* 4. Dr. Vieweg, Braunschweig, 231 pp.

WISE, D.U., 1963. An outrageous hypothesis for the tectonic pattern of the North American Cordillera. *Bull. Geol. Soc. Am.,* 74 : 357—362.

117

INDEX[1]

Acid matter, volcanic 50
Adriatic, 95
African Lake belt, 94, 109
AHLBURG, J., 48
AIRY, G.B., 10
Alaska, 89, 111, 112
—, earthquake in Anchorage, 112
Aleutian arc, 111
Aleutian Trench, 104
Alpine geosyncline, 95
Alps, 40, 41, 72
—, Australian, 90
—, Transsylvanian, 95
Amsterdam Island, 109
Anchorage, earthquake, 112
Andaman Islands, 47
ANDERSON, E.M., 2, 42, 44
Andes, 44, 83, 110, 113
—, earthquake, 83
—, Peruvian, 72
Annobom, 112
Anomalies, belt of strong negative, 36
—, free-air, 54
—, isostatic, Celebes Sea, 47
—, local isostatic gravity, Indonesia, 18
—, of outside gravity, corresponding to anomalies on a geoid, 33
—, of regional isostatic gravity, Indonesia, 19
Antillean arc, 86
Arabia, 109
Arc, Indonesian, 47
—, inner, 48, 50, 109
—, Caribbean, 47
—, second, 49
—, tectonic, 110
—, third, 75
—, volcanic, 48, 50
Ardennes, 40
Areas, joining, between wing and central parts, 49
ARGAND, E., 39
Ascension, 109
Asia, 50, 72, 86, 92, 103
Asia Islands, 72, 103
Atacama Trench, 83, 100

Atlas Mountains, 94
Atolls, straight rows of, 52
Australia, 72, 86, 89, 90
Azores, 34, 109

Baja California, 101
Balkan Mountains, 95
BÄR, C.B., 45, 89
Barbados, 50
Barisan, 45
Bartlett and Oriente Deeps, 54
Basalt, Bowen's theory of formation of, 58
Basins, in island-arc areas, 73
Belt, African Lake, 94
—, geosynclinal, 41, 92, 94
—, of graben, 44
—, of strong negative anomalies, 36
—, tectonic, 47, 49
—, third, 49
—, wing type, 50
Berlage, H.P., 86
BERNAL, J.D., 59
BIJLAARD, P.P., 35
BIRCH, F., 8
Bismarck Archipelago, 101
Bonin Trench, 101, 103
Border area, between continents and oceans, 72
—, between ur-continent and ur-ocean, 92
BORN, A., 84, 85, 87, 91, 93
Bougainville Island, 101
BOUGUER, P., 10
BOWEN, N.L., 58
BOWIE, W., 12
BROUWER, H.A., 38
Bruce Rock, 90
BRUINS, G.J., 81, 83
Buckling, Kuenen's experiments on, 37
Buenaventura, 83
Buena Vista oil field, 46
BULLARD, E.C., 25, 44
Burmah, 47, 72
Buru, 47

Caldeira, 55, 79
California 44, 101

---

[1] Authors names given in small capitals can be found in the reference list.

Canaries, 112
Cape Verde Islands, 112
Caribbean Islands, 47, 50
Caroline Islands, 110
Caroline Trench, 101, 103
Cascade, 111
Cayman Trough, 54
Celebes, 47
Celebes Sea, isostatic anomalies, 47
Cells, size of, 73
Central America, 51, 111
Central parts of island-arc, 47
Central ranges, 113
Central trenches, 48, 97
Chemical crust, 10
Chilean Andes, 83, 110, 113
Chilean coast, gravity profiles, 46
Chilean earthquake 1960, 83
Chiloé Island, 110
Christmas Island, 92, 109
Circular cells, 70
CLAIRAUT, A.C., 25, 26, 28, 34
Clapeyron's law, 60
Coal deposits, 97
Coast Range, 41
Colorado Plateau, 111
Compensating masses, 10
Compensation, local, 11
—, regional, 11
Compression, horizontal, 35
—, uniaxial, 47, 57
—, in the crust, 57
Conduction, slow, of heat, 72
Conductivity, thermal, 8
Continental drift, 52, 76
Continents, movements of, 59, 75
—, transport of, 52
Contraction theory, 57
Convection currents, 71
—, driving power of, 58
Convection current systems, distribution over
    the mantle, 59
—, under North America, 46
Cook Islands, 110
Cooling earth, 57
Core, 7
—, currents in the, 7
—, inner, 7
Coriolis effect, 7
CORON, S., 95
COULOMB, J., 82
Crust, below the oceans, 52
—, chemical, 10
—, chemical changes in the, 114
—, constitution of the, 9

—, continental, 55
—, down-buckling of the, 35, 97
—, extensive fields of uniaxial compression
    in the, 57
—, oceanic, 9, 51, 55
—, plastic down-buckling of the, 35
—, rigid, 10, 52
—, rise of, 40
—, shortening of, 41, 52
—, tension in the, 42, 55
—, thickening of the, 35
Crustal fault plane, 55
Crustal layer, upper, maximum tension in the,
    49
Crustal matter, excess of, 41
—, horizontal compression in the, 35
—, in mid-ocean rises, 9
—, uniaxial compression in the, 47
Crustal tension, Alpine arc – North Sea – the
    Channel, 44
Crustal wrench faulting, accompanied by
    overriding, 44
—, not accompanied by earthquakes, 46
Crystalline mantle, 61, 68
Cubic phase, 8
Cuneo, 95
Current system, 50
Currents, distribution of, 67
—, half turn, 9, 57
—, in a fluid earth, 67
—, in the core, 7
—, turbidity, 51
Cyclades, 95, 109

Darling Range, 90
DARWIN, G.H., 25, 28
Deep trenches, 97, 100
Deflections of the vertical, 10
Delta, Mississippi, 11
—, Nile, 11
DE SITTER, W., 25, 28
Development of a graben, 42
Deviations from equilibrium, 25
—, active volcanicity as a cause of, 34
Differentiation in the current system of a fluid
    earth, 67
Distribution, of convection-current systems
    over the mantle, 59
—, of current, 67
—, of geosynclines, 69
—, of volcanoes, 104, 105
Domodossola, 95
Down-buckling, of the crust, 35, 97
—, plastic, of the crust, 35, 52
DUTTON, C.E., 10

Dynamic stability, 9

Earth, cooling, 57
—, equilibrium figure of the, 25
—, external gravity field of the, 27
—, flattening of the, 34
—, fluid, 67
—, history of the, 65, 66, 67, 68, 70
—, mobility of the surface of the, 52
—, present period of the, 72, 80
Earthquake, Anchorage, 112
—, Andes, 83
—, Chilean 1960, 83
—, epicenters of, 82
—, San Francisco, 112
—, Tolten, 45, 46
East African lake zone, belt of graben, 44
Easter Island, 109
Ecuador–South Colombia group, 111
Eifel Mahren, 112
Elastic limit of the mantle, 71
Ellipsoid, rotation, 25
Emperor Sea Mounts, 109
Enstatite, 60
Epicenters of seisms, 82
Equilibrium, deviations from, 25, 34
—, isostatic, 10
—, readjustment towards, 11
Equilibrium figure of the earth, 25
Erosion, 114
Escarpments, Menard, 52, 86
Ethiopia, 109
Etna, 109
Europe, 72, 112
EWING, M., 81
Excess of crustal matter, 41

Fault, San Andreas, 112
Fault planes, parallel to mantle current, 50
Fault zone, situated on the inside of the arc, 49
Fennoscandia, rising curve, 61
Fernando Po, 112
Fields of uniaxial compression in the crust, 57
Fiji Islands, 110
First-order current in a fluid earth, 67
First phase of the earth's history, 66
Flattening of the earth, 34
Flow, pseudo, 8, 69, 72
Fluid earth, 67
Fourier development, 62
Fracture zone, Mendocino, 54
Free-air anomalies, 54
Freemantle, 90
Front Range, 41

Galapagos Islands, 109
Geoid, 33
Geomagnetic poles, 7
Geosynclinal belt, 92, 94
—, as a cause of mountain formation, 41
Geosynclinal ranges, 113
Geosynclines, alpine, 95
—, distribution of, 69
—, formation of, 70
—, oceanic, 75
Gilbert Islands, 110
Glacial period, 11
Graben, 42, 43, 44, 55, 57, 97, 114
—, development of, 42
Granite formation of, 42
Gravimetric cross-sections over a folded mountain range, 12
Gravity anomalies – anomalies on a geoid, 33
Gravity, isostatic, 18, 19
Gravity field, external, of the earth, 27
Gravity profiles, Chilean coast, 46
Great Dividing Range, 89
Great Glen Fault, 57, 112
Greece, 95
Grey Range, 90
GRIGGS, D., 73
Guatemala, 46, 101
GUTENBERG, B., 19, 46
Guyots, 55, 80

HAFNER, W., 42, 44
Half-graben, 90
Half-turn mantle currents, 9, 57
—, episodic, 71
HALLAM, A., 80
HAMILTON, E.L., 80
Harmonic development, spherical, 62
—, first order term, 65
—, of topographical elevations, 59
Harmonic, spherical, of fifth order, 69
—, of third order, 67
HARRISON, J.C., 54
Hawaiian group, 50, 109
HAYFORD, J.F., 12
Heat conduction, slow, 72
HEEZEN, B.C., 80
HEISKANEN, W.A., 10, 12, 27, 36, 43, 61, 66, 68
HESS, H.H., 80, 101, 102
Himalaya, 72
History of the earth, 65
—, first phase, 66
—, second phase, 67, 70
—, third (present) phase, 68, 70
Hokkaido, 88
Horizontal pressure gradient, 72

Horizontal wrench-faulting movements, 51
Horst, 43, 44, 114
HOSPERS, J., 83
Huber-Hencky, 69
HUMBERT, F.L., 51

Iceland, 109
Ideogeosyncline, 49
Indonesia, 18, 19, 34, 47, 72, 86
Inner arc, 48, 50, 109
Inner core, 7
Instability, potential, 71
Irian, West, 89
Island arc, 47
—, Indonesian and Caribbean, 47
—, not symmetrical, 47
Island-arc areas, deep basins in, 73
Isostatic equilibrium, 10
Isostatic readjustment between horst and graben in the Peel, 44
Isthmus, 51
Italy, 95
Ivrea, 95

Japan, 72, 88
Japan Trench, 101
Java, 47, 97
Java Trench, 103
JOBERT, G., 82
Joining areas between wing and central parts, 49

Kamchatka Peninsula, 88
Karafuto, 88
Kay Islands, 47
Kergoelen, 109
Kermadec Trench, 92
KING HUBBERT, M., 2, 42, 44
KRISHNAN, M.S., 92
KUENEN, PH.H., 36, 37, 51, 74
Kurile arc, 88
Kurile – Kamchatka arc, 111
Kurile Trench, 104

Laccadives, 109
Lake Belt, Africa, 94, 109
Lamont Geological Observatory, 46, 55
—, expeditions of, 83
Law, Clapeyron's, 60
Legendre term, 63
Lifting and erosion topography, 114
Limburg, 40, 97
—, rising of, 41
Lower Rhein graben, 97

MacDonnell Rangers, 90
Madeira, 50
Magnesium, 71
Magnetization of rocks, 52
Mahren, Eifel, 112
Malang–Tengger, 110
Maldives, 109
Mantle crystalline, 61, 68
—, distribution of convection current systems over the, 59
—, elastic limit of the, 71
—, main constituent of the, 8
Mantle convection currents, 8, 61
—, pattern of, 81
Mantle currents, 50, 57, 59, 63, 72
—, half-turn, 9, 57
—, below South America, 50
—, interrupted by periods of relaxation, 41
—, rising, 52, 79
—, rising limbs of, 55
Mantle current system, 70
—, rising under Asia, 50
—, large size, half-turn, 73
Mantle current – volcanic range angle, 114
Marianas Trench, 101, 103
Mascarenes, 109
Matterhorn, 95
Mauritius, 109
MEIJERING, J.L., 3, 8, 59
MENARD, H.W., 5, 52, 53, 86
Mendocino fracture zone, 54
Menard escarpments, 52, 86
MERCIER, J., 95
Merredin, 90
Mexican group, 111
Mexico, 44, 46, 101
Mid-Atlantic Rise, sounding profiles, 55
Mid-ocean rise, 9
Mindanao Trench, 45, 48, 97
Mississippi delta, 11
Mittelgebirge, 40, 58
—, topography, 114
Mobility, of the earth's surface, 52
—, of the Pacific Ocean floor, 80
Mont Blanc, 95
Monte Rosa, 95
Moon, attraction of, 67
Mountain formation, 113
—, caused by a geosynclinal belt, 41
Movements, parallel to tectonic belt, 49
—, of continents, 51, 59, 75
MULLER, J.J.A., 39

New England Range, 89
New Guinea, 44, 72, 88, 89

New Hebrides, 110
New Mexico group, 111
Newtonian fluid, 66
Newtonian viscosity mantle, 67
New Zealand, 92, 110
Nicobar Islands, 47
Nile Delta, 11
North America, 46, 51

Oil field, Buena Vista, 46
Olivine, 8, 59, 60
Orthorhombic phase, 8
Overriding, 44, 97

Pacific, 80
Palau Islands, 103
Panama, submarine ridge, 81
Paita, 83
Pattern of convection currents in the mantle, 81
Peel, the, 44
Peridotite, selective fusion of, 58
Persia, 72
Peruvian Andes, 83, 113
Philippine Islands, 44, 47, 88
Phoenix Islands, 110
Piedmont, 95
Planet Trench, 101
Plastic down-buckling in oceans, 52
Plastic flow, 69
Plateau Central, 112
Poles, geomagnetic, 7
Po valley, 95
PRATT, J.H., 10
Preanger, 110
Pressure gradient, horizontal, 72
PREY, A., 61, 65
Pseudo-flow, 8, 69, 72
Puerto Rico, 97
Puerto Rico Trench, 50
Pyrenees, 94

Rayleigh number, for a Newtonian viscosity mantle, 67
—, of mantle currents, 63
READ, H.H., 42
Readjustment, isostatic, between horst and graben in the Peel, 44
—, towards equilibrium, 11
Red Sea, 109
Reduction, indirect, 12
—, topographic and isostatic, 12
Regressions, 58
Relative movement of the Americas, 51
Réunion, 109

REVELLE, R., 80
Rhine, 40, 97
Rhône, 40
Ridges, mid-ocean, 52, 68, 80
—, submarine, Panama, 81
Rift, 55
Rigid crust, 10, 52
Rise, 40
—, Mid-Atlantic, 55
—, mid-ocean, 9
—, of foreland crust, 40
—, of Limburg, 41
—, of a horst, 43
Rising limbs of mantle currents, 55
Rising mantle currents, 52, 79
RITSEMA, A.R., 86
Rocks, magnetization of, 52
—, Tertiary, surface of, 97
Rocky Mountains, 41, 72
Rodriguez, 109
ROLLET, M., 95
Romanche Deep, 55, 79, 109
ROOYMANS, C.J.M., 3, 8, 59
Ross, A.D., 90
Rotation ellipsoid, 25
Rotation poles, 7
RUNCORN, S.K., 52, 59, 76

Sakhalin, 88
San Andreas Fault, 46, 57, 86, 112
San Salvador, 46, 101
Sardinia – Corsica ridge, 95
Satellite observations, 33
Second arc, of volcanic character, 49
Sectorial terms, 63
Seisms, epicenters of, 82
Seychelles, 109
SHEPARD, F.P., 80
Sicily, 95
Siebengebirge, 112
Sierra de Merida, 83
Sierra Nevada, 94
Snowy Mountain Range, 89
Society Islands, 110
Solomon Islands, 110
South America, 51, 81
—, west coast, 46
Spain, 94
Spherical harmonic development, 62
Spinel, 8, 59, 60
Stability, dynamic, 9
STAUB, R., 39, 40
St. Helena, 109
STOKES, G.G., 27, 32
St. Paul, 109

Stress deviator, 69
Stromboli, 95, 109
Submarine volcanoes, 55
Subsidence, of mid-ocean ridges, 80
—, of graben, 43
Substratum, 114
Sumatra, 47
Sumatra Trench, 45, 48, 97, 103
Sunda Strait, 49
Surface of Tertiary rocks, 97

Talaud Islands, 47
TALWANI, M., 54, 101
Tanimbar Islands, 47
Tapanuli, triangulation, 39
TAYLOR, F.B., 52
Tectonic arc, 110
Tectonic belt, 47
—, movements parallel to, 49
Tension, in the crust, 42, 49, 55
Term, first order, 65
—, third order, 67
—, fifth order, 69, 70
—, sectorial, 63
—, tesseral, 63
Ternary system of matter in transition layers, 60
Tesseral terms, 63
Tethys geosynclinal belt, 92, 94
The Netherlands, levelling of, 41
Theorem, of Clairaut, 26, 34
—, of Stokes, 27
Theory, contraction, 57
Thermal conductivity, 8
Third arcs, 75
Third belt, 49
Timor area, 110
Timor Trough, 47
TISSERAND, F., 25
Tobago, 50
Tolten, earthquake, 45, 46
Tonga Islands, 110
Tonga Trench, 92
Tonga – Kermadec Trench, 101
Topography, lifting and erosion, 114
Transgressions, 58
Transition layer, 59, 60, 61
Transport of continents, 52
Trenches, 45, 48, 50, 83, 92, 97, 100, 101, 103, 104
—, central, 48, 97
—, wing, 48, 97
Triangulation, Tapanuli, after an earthquake, 39

Trinidad, 50
Tristan da Cunha, 109
Tuamotu, 109
Turbidity currents, 51
Tuscarora Deep, 88
Types of deep trenches, 97, 100

Ulithi Atoll, 103
UMBGROVE, J.H.F., 19, 49
Uniaxial compression, 47, 57
Upper Rhein graben, 97

Valdivia, 81
Valdivia and Chiloé Island, 45
VAN WIJNEN, J.C., 83
VELDKAMP, J., 86
Venezuela, 83
VENING MEINESZ, F.A., 10, 12, 19, 27, 36, 43, 45, 46, 55, 61, 66, 68, 69, 70, 74, 75, 81, 83, 90, 96, 98, 99, 100, 101, 103
VÉRONNET, A., 25
VERSTAPPEN, H.TH., 45, 89
Vertical, deflections of the, 10
Vesuvius, 109
VISSER, S.W., 86
Volcanic, activity, 112
—, arc, 48
—, islands, 55
Volcanic-island arc, acid matter thrown out by volcans of, 50
Volcanic range – mantle current angle, 114
Volcanicity, as a cause of deviations from equilibrium, 34
Volcanoes, distribution of, 104, 105
—, Ethiopian, 109
—, Indonesian, 18
—, submarine, 55

Waigeo, 103
WEGENER, A., 52, 59, 76
West Irian, 89
Wing ranges, 49, 113
Wing trenches, 48, 97
WISE, D.U., 111
Wrench faulting, 113
—, combined with overriding, 97
—, crustal, 44, 46
—, horizontal movements, 51

Yellowstone Park, 111

Zonal term, 63

PRINTED IN THE NETHERLANDS